THE MARIA THUN BIODYNAMIC CALENDAR 2021

CREATED BY MARIA AND MATTHIAS THUN

Floris Books

Floris Books is proud to be part of the international biodynamics movement. We aim to support biodynamic farmers, small-holders, wine-makers and gardeners by publishing informative and inspiring books, calendars and apps.

Compiled by Matthias Thun
Translated by Bernard Jarman
Additional astronomical material
by Wolfgang Held and Christian Maclean

Published in German under the title *Aussaattage*
English edition published by Floris Books

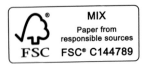

MIX
Paper from
responsible sources
FSC   FSC® C144789

British Library CIP Data available
ISBN 978-178250-654-6
ISSN: 2052-5761
Printed in Poland through Hussar

Walter Thun, Flowering Willow in Willingshausen, *(watercolour, 30 x 40 cm)*

The dynamic quality of this simple and eye-catching painting of a willow is enhanced by the diagonal lines of the branches meeting those of the riverbank.

Introduction

The planetary effects in the monthly notes for 2019/2020 were as expected. Not only was it difficult for plants to cope with the drought in many parts of the world, the lack of water reduced the nectar flow in the flowers, and there was, for example, virtually no honeydew. This limited the swarming drive among bee colonies too. The forests also struggled with the drought; it hindered the formation of tree resin and made the trees more susceptible to numerous pests. For bees the year was underwhelming, while for many a forester and woodland farmer the year was a shock. For 2020/2021 we therefore hope for more rain.

Easter 2019

Matthias Thun

During 2019 we received many questions concerning the date of Easter. We had in our calendar simply followed the accepted date of Easter as April 21. Easter is the first Sunday after the first Full Moon after the spring equinox. In practice it is calculated by a series of tables devised by the mathematician Carl Friedrich Gauss in the early nineteenth century, and assumes the spring equinox to be on March 21.

However, in 2019 the spring equinox was actually on March 20 (at 21:58 GMT), and if we strictly follow the astronomical rule rather than the tabular calculation, the first Full Moon was on Thursday March 21 at 1:42 (GMT), and so Easter would be on Sunday March 24.

To make matters more complicated, we could of course ask, why should the time (and date) of Greenwich be used? Should it not be in Jerusalem? Using the local time of Jerusalem, the equinox would indeed be on March 21 (just after midnight). Should then the Full Moon occurring on the same date be used, or should it be the Full Moon on a date *after* the equinox?

In short, the date of Easter in 2019 was ambiguous. Which date would actually affect the world of plants and animals? We sought some guidance from the climatic phenomena but unfortunately to no avail. In previous years it was possible to recognise the transition from Good Friday to Easter Sunday through, for example, the behaviour of birds. In 2019 however, neither of the two possible dates gave a definitive indication.

We therefore decided to carry out comparative trials around both dates. The plants we used were spring oats, spring rye, tomatoes, cucumbers, peppers and radishes.

As the chosen dates approached a few minor problems presented themselves. That spring, which had begun quite mild, was not conducive to steady and even plant growth. Right up until March 20 we had repeated night frosts. During the first trial period from March 21 to 24 it was sunny but the night frosts and a light sprinkling of snow prevented any outdoor sowing. In order to germinate vegetable plants require an ongoing night-time temperature of at least 3–4°C (36–37°F). If frost interrupts the process of germination it will stop and in a subsequent warm period germination will not occur evenly because the seeds cannot repeat their initial push to germinate.

All our sowings therefore had to take place in the greenhouse. This was no problem for the vegetable seeds and plants. Only for the cereals, which are normally sown directly where they are to mature, did we have to find another solution. They were sown in larger box containers that could be planted out four weeks later during the second trial period.

In the second period the cereals were sown directly outside and the vegetables were sown in the greenhouse and transplanted outside later. Sowing the various seeds in spring under the same conditions at an interval of four weeks with varying weather was clearly no easy matter.

Since we had to reckon with a spring that did not progress harmoniously and the Easter sowing dates were fixed, we had at least to ensure there was sufficient frost-free soil available. We therefore calculated the amount of soil needed and prepared a mix.

Soil was needed for the greenhouse bed and for the plant pots and boxes. To make a good mixture one third was well rotted, two-year-old cow manure compost, one third meadow soil and one third organic seed compost that was bought in. These were thoroughly mixed and in the process repeatedly treated with barrel preparation (cow pat pit, CPP) so that the soil from outside could benefit from the compost preparations.

The soil mix was left for about four weeks so that its three components could form a single entity. Because the barrel preparation leads to a good composting and transformation process, it is essential that horn manure is applied when the seeds are sown in order to halt the rotting and fungal processes. Without the horn manure there is a danger that the composting processes in the soil will transfer to the plants and cause fungal problems.

Horn manure preparation should be sprayed three times. The first application should be made in the appropriate constellation (for instance, Fruit times for tomato). Then the cosmic effect is strengthened and is more visible in the plants. In biodynamic agriculture horn silica is normally sprayed at the appropriate stage of growth to improve quality. In these particular trials we have refrained from using it because the silica application could mask the effects of the Easter constellations.

Previous trials had shown that the effects would only be seen in the next plant generation. This means collecting seeds from the cereals and tomatoes, for example, and growing them the following year. The observations and experiences of previous years lead us to hope that similar observations could be made again.

Friedrich with the single grains. Sowing vegetable seeds during the first Easter dates. Left: Maundy Thursday, right: Good Friday Later it was found that the first seeds sown in a taller plant pot thrived better before being pricked out.

Titia sows oats in tubs where they produced fine deep roots.

Friedrich sowing oats in the greenhouse bed.

Friedrich sowing tomatoes in the greenhouse.

Horn manure is applied to the seed beds to ensure that the soil composting process set in motion by the barrel preparation is ended.

We have found time and again that the days immediately preceeding Easter tend to be somewhat oppressive and that on Easter Sunday the tension is released. On Easter Sunday at dawn the birds suddenly come out in full song. I was outside at dawn during both of the trial 'Easter' periods but this year the birds remained silent. On the second Easter date however two wagtails showed by their delightful pairing behaviour, that something had changed in their cycle of life.

In conversations with various friends about the two Easter dates, some of whom had also carried out sowing trials and wanted to experience the mood, I found that similar experiences had been made. Significant differences were, however, also presented which could be traced back to the Moon constellations of those days or else to feelings that arose.

Whether we will succeed with the help of the plants and their subsequent progeny in finding the answer to the engima of the date of Easter in 2019 will only be clear after two growing seasons. We have come to realise over many years that we cannot rely solely on weather phenomena, but that only through the next plant generation can there be any certainty. The resulting harvest can therefore only be reported on in the next calendar.

Stirring the preparations. We stir small quantities in cylindrical earthenware pots.

Horn manure is also applied to the seeds sown into the greenhouse soil.

More on Planets and Trees

In reflecting on the 2020 edition of the *Maria Thun Biodynamic Calendar,* we would like to expand upon what was presented regarding the connection between trees and planets and the reference made by Rudolf Steiner to the way planetary forces are expressed in fruiting trees.

While woody plants are of course also dependent on the Sun they have a much stronger connection to the planets in our solar system. In the Agriculture Course Rudolf Steiner refers to the connection of conifers to Saturn and the oak tree to Mars. Later on, in the second lecture, he said: 'Just like the colour of flowers, the fine taste of apricots or plums is a cosmic quality that has made its way up into the fruit. In every apple you are actually eating Jupiter, in every plum, Saturn.' (p. 40).

In other places he describes the living relationship between the tree and the forces of the stars. In the case of woody plants we often find in the fruit the planetary influences expressed from the previous year. This has led us and some of our readers to ask whether a fruit-like quality can be found in shrubs that don't bear edible fruits.

When working with different types of wood we soon discover that they emit wonderful smells. These scents often help overcome feelings of indisposition associated with many an ailment. We have also noted elsewhere how a strong flow of nectar can be detected in the evening air beside beehives as the nectar is being transformed to honey. This scent has a crystal-like quality, strengthening our innermost self.

When describing evolution Rudolf Steiner describes how during the Atlantean epoch the foundation of the human self and self-awareness was being developed in parallel with the formation of the six-sided crystal – an amazing complementary creative process.

Maples

The living fluid of the maple, the blood of the tree, is a resource that can be tapped at certain times of year and thickened into maple syrup.

It is not honey that is formed from the nectar of flowers, but the sieved liquid sap containing about 3% sugar which then has to undergo an elaborate process to produce a thickened syrup. The maple honey originating from the nectaries of the flowers (all flowers have them) is of a higher value since it is produced in the nectaries of flowers during certain planetary aspects.

Teas can also be made from the flowers, enabling Jupiter forces to be taken up. Passionate herb tea drinkers will, however, miss a strong flavour. The taste of maple tea is very subtle and unassuming. It can however be strengthened with a 'taste enhancer' in the form of flower honey. Only a very small amount of honey

A red and a yellow maple tree. In spring the glistening pale colour of the yellow maples is particularly striking. They produce so much nectar that other flowers which bloom at the same time such as rape are often neglected by the bees.

Red maple flowers

Yellow maple flowers

Maple flower buds

Green, unripe maple seeds

should be added – not more than ¼ teaspoonful per cup. Other forms of sugar or maple syrup should be avoided since it is only maple honey which can bring out the flavour. Beet sugar should likewise be avoided since its earthy, root qualities overpower the fine nuances of flavour. This also applies to the blossom teas described below.

Elder flowers

Elderberries

Elderflower tea. The flower teas can be made from fresh or dried flowers. A good tasting syrup can be produced from elderberries. Once they are ripe the berries need to be harvested quickly before the birds eat them.

The First Nine Years of Research

Maria Thun

Introduction by Matthias Thun

By way of an introduction and to make it easier to understand the very difficult texts written by Maria Thun about the first nine years of research, some background will be given regarding the historical context out of which the decision was made to investigate, understand and verify influences from the cosmos.

In the immediate aftermath of the Second World War an attempt was made in many fields of life to rethink the thoughts and ideas inherited from the past. Rudolf Steiner's Agricultural Course had taken place in 1924 and the questions which had arisen in relation to agriculture before the war could now be taken up and put into practice. Rudolf Steiner placed much emphasis on the importance of enlivening the soil with the help of special preparations and on the influence of the cosmos on living processes.

The old farming rules inherited from the past still lived strongly in the minds of farmers and gardeners and it was believed that new astronomical questions could find answers and build on this old knowledge. It very quickly became apparent, however, that the old farming rules were no longer effective and often appeared to be false. It is worth pointing out that those rules were not wrong; it was just that the constellations with which they had been connected were not known.

Maria Thun knew from her parents that in their youth the many tasks in the garden and on the fields determined by weather phenomena were carried out at particular times. Having learnt from Rudolf Steiner about the close connection between plant life and the cosmos she began the experiments that are described in the following text. These initial trials laid the foundation for the later successive planting trials that are being continued on our farm to this day.

Sowing with Moon phases and nodes

In the Agriculture Course Rudolf Steiner pointed out very specific areas where plant growth is influenced by the planets. He pointed particularly to the forces of the Full Moon and how they work beneficially on the growth of young seedlings. These indications were taken up by many people engaged with biodynamic agriculture and put into practice. In this way Franz Rulni together with Heinrich Schmidt produced a sowing calendar that focused particularly on the phases, nodes, perigee and apogee and on the ascending and descending cycles of the Moon.

In applying the recommendations of Franz Rulni in 1952 I made the following observations. Within one Full Moon period there were around ten days indicated as being good sowing days. It so happened that during this time radish seeds from the same seed packet were sown on four different days. I noticed very early on that the seedlings displayed uneven growth patterns and as they developed, evolved quite distinct characteristics. Finding the cause of this development became a burning quest for me. So I then decided to carry out some daily sowing trials in the hope of solving the riddle.

The trials were set up on well cultivated (biodynamic) sandy soil with plenty of humus. It soon became apparent that different preceding crops altered the otherwise uniform results. So in order to have sufficient land available with the same preceding crop we had to take on additional garden areas. The soils were all treated with ripe compost that had received the biodynamic compost preparations. The horn manure preparation was only applied in spring and autumn – a daily application for every sowing would have been impossible and might also have altered the plants' characteristics.

In the beginning a piece of land was cultivated and the seed bed prepared in advance. I then sowed a row of a certain number of seeds each day. After a while we found that while seeds sown on the first days had some variation, as time went on they became more and more uniform.

New issues were thus appearing that were not so easy to solve. A new bed had meanwhile been set up to undertake a further month of sowings and once again the same phenomenon occurred. After much heart searching we came to realise that it might have to do with the moment when the ground had been prepared. From then on we cultivated narrow strips and prepared the seed bed on the day we sowed the seeds. We soon saw considerable variation.

Further challenges then confronted us. A dry period occurred with a lot of hot weather. Traditional practice meant that the radish beds had to be irrigated. The result was that all the rows looked nearly identical. The only differences were in size due to the date of sowing, otherwise only the effects of watering could be seen. These experiences led us to decide that all future sowings would be left to the mercy of the weather. The only interventions would be hoeing and weeding. This was the basis upon which all future growing trials would be carried out.

I had discovered meanwhile that the development of a plant's root system proceeded in rhythmic way. This raised a new question: If the part of the plant which is above the earth is stimulated by the forces of the Full Moon, does it not follow that root growth is stimulated by the forces of the New Moon? This was not something readily visible in seedlings germinating in water.

I felt that the broad bean with its strong root would be a suitable plant to test. So I planted a few beans outside each day and kept them under observation. I thought after a few months that I had already discovered the rhythm – root growth always began on the day of the descending Moon node. Since the various lunar and planetary cycles were still a mystery for me, I was delighted by my discovery. The summer came and went and winter brought a pause to my investigations. The work was taken up again the following year. Now we found that this time root development began the day after the Moon node. This was very disappointing but it also made us determined to finally solve the problem. This cycle connected to the forming of roots had in the meantime unlocked new practical possibilities for the grower in terms of saving time when pricking out seedlings during the growing season.

The year 1956 came around and broad beans were again planted from early spring. The phenomena of the previous year repeated themselves. During the course of the autumn the time difference increased further and by the following year root growth started a full three days after the Moon node. We then realised that making a link to the Moon node was a mistake.

Ascending and descending Moon

I felt it necessary then to study lunar and planetary rhythms more intensely. I soon discovered that when the first root observation had been made, the Moon was at its highest position in the zodiac and that this occurred one day before the Moon node. It remained on that day for a while and then in succeeding years was delayed by one, two or three days as the node gradually moved through the zodiac. The day in question was therefore determined by the sidereal Moon rhythm which in turn depends on the position of the Moon in the zodiac. At the time the node was positioned in the constellation of Gemini. This solved the mystery but further evidence was needed for it to be conclusive. Various types of cutting including runners from house plants and hyacinths, were then taken, put in water to root and observed over a long period. Parallel trials were also carried out on open ground with lettuce, cabbage, celery and annual flowers.

The effect of the descending Moon (that is, when the Moon's daily arcs become lower as it descends from the constellation of Gemini to Scorpio) was always confirmed and even strengthened when the descending forces of the day were used as well. Time and again we could observe how plants transplanted in the afternoon during the descending Moon needed to be watered only once at the moment of planting and would then grow on unhindered.

This process can be further improved if the plants are taken out of the ground in the morning while they are still subject to the ascending forces of the day, kept cool and moist over midday and then transplanted in the afternoon. Overnight the plants are then able to immediately orientate themselves to their new position and stand fresh and upright the next day. In comparison with plants of the same species remaining in the seed bed, there was better growth and vitality throughout the growing season. Plants of the same species transplanted during an ascending Moon period often struggle for days or even weeks. The outer leaves wilt and only with a great deal of effort is the plant able to renew itself out of its growing point. In practice such plants frequently require ongoing watering and a delay of several weeks can be detected in their overall development.

The Moon in the zodiac

Taking account of our ongoing experiences we continued with regular sowings of radish under the same parameters. A certain underlying principle could now be identified. However, we lacked the ability to read it. We found for example how the same type of plant developed over a period of two, three or sometimes four days. In one case there would be a strong root with very small leaves (Root type). In another there would be massive leaf development with relatively small roots (Leaf type). In the third case the plant developed a reddish stem and rapidly developed flowers which remained for a relatively long time but developed virtually no roots (Flower type). There was a fourth type which appeared to be in even more of a hurry. Forming roots seemed completely unnecessary, nor was much time spent on growing leaves. It was in a great hurry to produce flowers and then move on into producing seeds and reproducing (Fruit/Seed type).

A clear fourfold quality was revealed in the plant. This wasn't easy to find at first because we were convinced that the plant manifests itself in terms of the threefold organs of root, leaf and flower. The fourfold qualities that were found repeat themselves three times in the course of a month.

I suddenly realised that I might have found a basic law of life determining the way a plant is formed. Did those original breeders of our cultivated plants have an insight into this law? Gaining knowledge of this membering is an unimaginable reward for all these years of effort.

During the quiet days of winter I set about working through all these results in order to discover the origin of these formative processes. This led to the discovery that as the Moon passes from one constellation of the zodiac to the next, the plant type changes. I drew this pictorially and graphically and recalled to my amazement that I had seen a related differentiation of zodiac forces in a presentation given by Guenther Wachsmuth when he spoke about the etheric formative forces that stream out from the zodiac. These correlate in the following way:

Wachsmuth's observation		My plant observations
Life ether	Taurus	Root formation
Life ether	Virgo	Root formation
Life ether	Capricorn	Root formation
	Earth forces	
Chemical ether	Pisces	Leaf formation
Chemical ether	Cancer	Leaf formation
Chemical ether	Scorpio	Leaf formation
	Watery forces	
Light ether	Gemini	Flower formation
Light ether	Libra	Flower formation
Light ether	Aquarius	Flower formation
	Light forces	
Warmth ether	Aries	Fruit formation
Warmth ether	Leo	Fruit formation
Warmth ether	Sagittarius	Fruit formation
	Warmth forces	

The logical consequence is that plant growth is stimulated by one of the four etheric forces relating to the classical elements of Earth, Water, Air and Fire, through certain lunar forces depending on the Moon's position in the zodiac (as with my plant observations). The Moon takes on the role of mediator – at least in terms of the cultivated plant species (radishes) that have been observed – between the realm of the fixed stars and the elements of plant growth.

We then tried to understand what caused an upset to the processes of growth on certain days. We found that the Moon's perigee almost always has a negative effect and that the days of the Moon nodes are often unfavourable. They were found to cause blockages to growth. Other influences which override a particular plant type arise through planetary oppositions. The opposition of Venus and Jupiter, for example, encouraged a powerful flowering impulse.

Radishes from Leaf times

Trials with other plants

Many new questions arose, in particular, how do these forces affect other culti-vated plants – or is perhaps only the radish a suitable medium? The challenge now was to test 'typical' representative plants. During the following years tests were carried out on carrots, parsnips and salsify as Root crops; lettuce, spinach, corn salad, cress and, to a small extent, cabbages as Leaf plants; zinnias, snap-dragons and asters as Flowers; and beans, peas, cucumbers and to a small extent tomatoes as Fruiting plants.

Prepared plant compost was applied, and in spring and autumn the horn ma-nure preparation. Horn silica was not used, but since then we have found that when it is used intensively the quality of plant type can be enhanced.

The experiences made with radishes were confirmed with other annual plant species. It was often difficult to discover significant differences in the early growth stages of a plant but on reaching maturity the result always came out the same. Root vegetables that were sown when the Moon was in Taurus, Virgo and Capricorn developed the best roots as well as the most harmonious structure and flavoursome quality while the upper part of the plant remained relatively small. With Root vegetables sown at Leaf times there was vigorous leaf devel-opment and small roots whose keeping quality was moderate. Roots shrivelled quite early during storage unlike those sown at Root times which kept in the sand well into spring and had a somewhat salt-like structure. Root vegetables sown at Flower and Fruit times had very finely divided leaves while the roots were often stringy and sometimes even slightly woody. In the warm year of 1959 several of them even went to seed.

Plants which are valued primarily for their leaves such as spinach, lettuce, corn salad and cress (cabbage family) thrive best when sown with the Moon in Pisces, Cancer and Scorpio. These plants develop a mass of leaves and re-

Radishes from Root times

main at the leaf stage without going rapidly to seed. If the plants are left too long they start to tiller – a sign that the reproductive power is retained in the leaf realm. This latter symptom is observed most strongly with sowings in Cancer and Scorpio. In this way it is possible to sow corn salad and spinach from spring through to late autumn without fear of the plants bolting. Another small difference could be observed in that sowings made before St John's tide in Cancer and Scorpio and after St John's in Pisces, had the greater leaf mass.

In the case of snapdragons, asters and zinnias we made the following observations: Sowings made in Pisces, Cancer and Scorpio resulted in a large amount of leaf growth but flowering only occurred with great difficulty; one could say there was a certain 'flowering laziness'. Sown at Fruit times these plants rapidly produced a few tiny leaves, went quickly to flower and then formed seed. The most harmonious Flowering plants came from sowings made with the Moon in Gemini, Libra and Aquarius. Branching clumps developed with a plethora of flower buds and the plants remained in the flowering state for a long period. Flowers can be cut continuously for the plant is always producing new side shoots. There is a pronounced propensity for flowering. Flowers sown at Root times have a meagre growth above ground and little tendency for flowering.

In observing the Fruiting plants new questions emerged. We found that although the constellations of Aries and Sagittarius were particularly favourable for developing the fleshy fruits of cucumbers, tomatoes and beans, the harvest of ripe peas and beans was not so satisfactory. For a good crop of ripe peas and broad beans the Moon in Leo was found to be best. When cucumbers, beans and tomatoes were sown with the Moon in Leo the plants went through their young growth stage and very quickly formed fruits with large seeds. I made the provisional assumption that this was the result of other influences – which is why new trials were continually being set up. We had found a fourfoldness – was this now being put in question?

Sown at Leaf times cucumbers, tomatoes and beans responded with the now familiar phenomenon – a huge amount of leaf growth and low propensity to flower. We found time and again that at Flower times cucumbers produced a large number of male flowers but very few fruit-bearing female flowers. At these different times the plant was actually only able to reproduce its own kind which for the gardener of course, is not enough. While the above-mentioned plants produced very desirable fruits when sown with the Moon in Aries and Sagittarius, only very poor growth above the earth occurred when Root times were used. Symptoms of congestion were repeatedly visible and this often led to an attack of aphids.

We found that climbing beans sown during the descending Root constellation of Virgo produced a huge root mass, the roots went very deep, grew thick as turnips and consisted to a great extent of nitrogen nodules. Something similar was found to be the case with peas and broad beans. These were the best times for sowing green manure crops too – their value is found in the root mass.

Further observations of fruit crops sown in Leo, Sagittarius and Aries showed that a distinction can be made between fruit and seed crops – there is in effect a fivefoldness whereby Sagittarius and Aries are Fruit times and Leo a Seed time.

Other observations

While writing down my observations from the summer of 1962 I discovered a lecture given in another context by Rudolf Steiner on January 1, 1912, where he describes the fivefold plant and its therapeutic effect on the human being. He pointed to the healing effect of plant seeds on the human heart. Elsewhere he also showed that within the physical body the region of the heart has its origin in the constellation of Leo. It is therefore remarkable yet quite fitting to discover that a plant medicine for the heart is formed and influenced by the same constellation.

This discovery gave me the courage to make the results of my work more widely available to those active in biodynamic agriculture. I am of course aware that there is still much to be discovered. The perennial plants, cereals, trees and other things all need to be carefully observed and then other rhythms will come into play.

From the outset the work which has been described demanded a precise observation of atmospheric conditions, the weather and also the micro-climate which is influenced by the lay of the land, the way dew forms, the breathing of the earth, wind direction, retention of warmth, and so on. In the process it became clear that the longer term weather conditions are determined by the movement of the planets through the various regions of the zodiac. Interruptions and disturbances are the result of conjunctions and oppositions. Hence the earthquakes we have experienced in recent years have always occurred during Neptune quadratures (square aspect) while powerful thunderstorms are prominent during a Uranus quadrature.

The etheric qualities which can be observed in the micro-climate on the other hand, are strongly connected with the passage of the Moon through the zodiac. The formation of dew and mist at Water times is completely different to that at Warmth times. When the Moon is transiting Pisces, Cancer and Scorpio the sky is generally grey and overcast and if this is reinforced by longer term influences, then rain is to be expected at those times. If it is not supported by the moisture bringing influences of the planets then a layer of mist will at least bring more moisture than at other times. During periods of drought it is possible to retain this moisture using appropriate soil cultivations. During cold and damp periods we have always observed how the atmosphere at Warmth and Light times has quite a different quality than at Water or Earth times. It is possible in this way to bring more warmth and light into the soil and retain or release moisture depending on what the plants require.

Work on the crop after transplanting

In the early years we found that seed bed preparation on the day of sowing had a significant effect on the development of the plant. This led to the question, can the particular crop type be further supported by cultivating the soil at the corresponding times?

The results described above came from humus-containing sandy soils and later on from clay soil. Both soils had been under well-managed biodynamic cultivation.

During the course of the sowing trials an ever stronger response from the plants to these cosmic rhythms could be observed. Once these results had attained a certain level of accuracy they were passed on for other people to try. When checking these myself I came to realize that the response of strongly mineralised soils to these finer influences was minimal, while good humus-rich soils of whatever type were capable of responding strongly to these forces.

The question has often been put, what is a living soil? Here it became visible – a soil which as a result of applying well-prepared compost, possesses the power to absorb cosmic influences, transform them into positive formative processes and enable the plant itself to activate forces from the stars and thereby create the quality nutrition that human beings need.

Background to the Calendar

The zodiac

The **zodiac** is a group of twelve constellations of stars which the Sun, Moon and all the planets pass on their circuits. The Sun's annual path always takes exactly the same line, called **ecliptic.**

The angles between the Sun, Moon and planets are called **aspects.** In this calendar the most important is the 120° angle, or trine.

In the illustration below the outer circle shows the varying sizes of the visible **constellations** of the zodiac. The dates on this outer circle are the approximate dates on which the Sun enters the constellation (from year to year the actual date can change by one day because of leap years). The inner circle shows the divisions into equal sections of 30° corresponding to the **signs** used in astrology.

It is the *constellations,* not the signs, on which our observations are based, and which are used throughout this calendar.

The twelve constellations are grouped into four different types, each having three constellations at an angle of about 120°, or trine. About every nine days the Moon passes from one type – for instance Root – through the other types (Flower, Leaf and Fruit) back to the same type again.

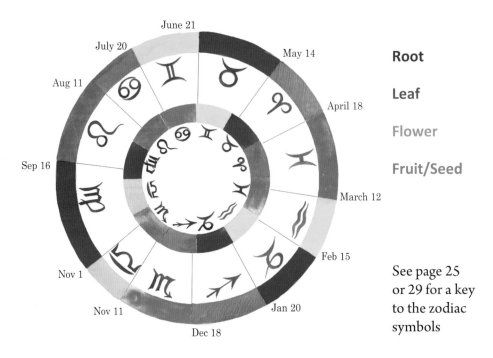

Root

Leaf

Flower

Fruit/Seed

See page 25 or 29 for a key to the zodiac symbols

22

What are oppositions, trines, conjunctions and nodes?

Oppositions ☍

A **geocentric** (Earth-centred) **opposition** occurs when for the observer on the Earth there are two planets opposite one another – 180° apart – in the heavens. You cannot see both planets at opposition – one will be above the horizon, the other below. They look at one another from opposite sides of the sky and their light interpenetrates. Their rays fall on to the Earth and stimulate in a beneficial way the seeds that are being sown in that moment. In our trials we have found that seeds sown at times of opposition resulted in a higher yield of top quality crops.

At times of opposition two zodiac constellations are also playing their part. If one planet is standing in a Warmth constellation, the second one will usually be in a Light constellation or vice versa. If one planet is in a Water constellation, the other will usually be in an Earth one. (As the constellations are not equally sized, the point opposite may not always be in the opposite constellation.)

With a heliocentric (Sun-centred) opposition the Sun is in the centre and the two planets placed 180° apart also gaze at each other but this time across the Sun. Their rays are also felt by the Earth and stimulate better plant growth. However, heliocentric oppositions are not shown or taken into account in the calendar.

Trines △ or ▲

The twelve constellations are grouped into four different types, each having three constellations at an angle of about 120°, or trine. About every nine days the Moon passes a similar region of forces.

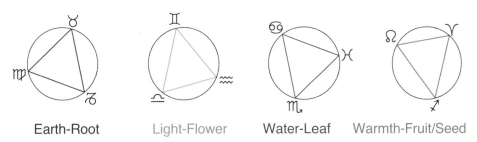

Earth-Root   Light-Flower   Water-Leaf   Warmth-Fruit/Seed

Trines occur when planets are 120° from one another. The two planets are then usually both standing in the same elemental configuration – Aries and Leo for example are both Warmth constellations. A Warmth trine means that the effects of these constellations will enhance fruit and seed formation in the plants sown at this time. If two planets are in trine position in Water, watery influences will be enhanced, which usually brings high rainfall. Plants sown at these times will yield more leaf than those at other times. Trine effects can change the way plants grow.

Sometimes when two planets are in a trine, they are in different types of constellations. These are shown as △ under planetary aspects, but have no effect on plant growth and are not shown as coloured ▲ in the left-hand pages.

Conjunctions ☌

Conjunctions occur when two or more planets stand behind one another in space. It is then usually only the planet closest to the Earth that has any influence on plant growth. If this influence is stronger than that of the Moon, cosmic disturbances can occur that irritate the plant and cause checks in growth. This negative effect is increased further when the Moon or another planet stands directly in front of another – an occultation (•) or eclipse in the case of Sun and Moon. Sowing at these times will affect subsequent growth detrimentally and harm a plant's regenerative power.

Nodes ☊ and ☋

The Moon's and planets' paths vary slightly, sometimes above and sometimes below the ecliptic. The point at which their paths cross the ecliptic is called a node (☊ is the symbol for ascending node, and ☋ for the descending node). Nodes cause unfavourable times of varying lengths.

If a New Moon is at a node there is a solar eclipse, as the Moon is directly in front of the Sun, while a Full Moon at a node causes a lunar eclipse where the Earth's shadow falls on the Moon. If the Sun or Moon pass exactly in front of a planet, there is an occultation (•). If Mercury or Venus pass exactly in front of the Sun, this is a transit (other planets cannot pass in front of the Sun).

The effects of the Moon

In its 27-day orbit round the Earth, the Moon passes through the constellations of the zodiac and transmits forces to the Earth which affect the four elements: Earth, Light (Air), Water and Warmth (Fire). They in turn affect the four parts of the plant: the roots, the flower, the leaves and the fruit or seeds. The health and growth of a plant can therefore be stimulated by sowing, cultivating and harvesting it in tune with the cycles of the Moon.

These cosmic forces can also be harnessed in beekeeping. By opening and closing the bee 'skep' or box in rhythm with the Moon, the bees' activity is directly affected.

The table below summarises the effects of the movement of the Moon through the twelve constellations on plants, bees and the weather.

The amount of time the Moon spends in any constellation varies between two and four days. However, this basic framework can be disrupted by planetary oppositions which override the normal tendencies; equally, it may be that trine positions (see pp. 23f) activate a different elemental force to the ones the Moon is transmitting. Times when the Moon's path or a planet's path intersects with the ecliptic (ascending ☊ or descending ☋ node; see page 24) are subject to mainly negative effects. These are intensified if there is an eclipse or occultation, in which case the nearer planet interrupts the influence of the distant one. Such times are unsuitable for sowing or harvesting.

Constellation	Sign	Element	Plant	Bees	Weather
Pisces, Fishes	♓	W Water	Leaf	Making honey	Damp
Aries, Ram	♈	H Warmth	Fruit	Gathering nectar	Warm/hot
Taurus, Bull	♉	E Earth	Root	Building comb	Cool/cold
Gemini, Twins	♊	L Light	Flower	Gathering pollen	Airy/bright
Cancer, Crab	♋	W Water	Leaf	Making honey	Damp
Leo, Lion	♌	H Warmth	Fruit	Gathering nectar	Warm/hot
Virgo, Virgin	♍	E Earth	Root	Building comb	Cool/cold
Libra, Scales	♎	L Light	Flower	Gathering pollen	Airy/bright
Scorpio, Scorpion	♏	W Water	Leaf	Making honey	Damp
Sagittarius, Archer	♐	H Warmth	Fruit	Gathering nectar	Warm/hot
Capricorn, Goat	♑	E Earth	Root	Building comb	Cool/cold
Aquarius, Waterman	♒	L Light	Flower	Gathering pollen	Airy/bright

Good Friday to Easter

Easter is a date set by astronomical events: it is determined by the Full Moon after the spring equinox. Our experience and trials over the last 40 years have shown that Good Friday and the Saturday are not good times for sowing or transplanting. Seeds sown on those days germinate poorly, plants transplanted on these days don't root properly and most don't survive. This negative effect on plant growth begins in the early morning of Good Friday and ends at sunrise on Easter Sunday, *local time*. This is why these days are marked as unfavourable in the calendar. Remember to apply *local time* for this effect, as the unfavourable time shown is for Britain and Ireland.

Groupings of plants for sowing and harvesting

When we grow plants, different parts are cultivated for food. We can divide them into four groups.

Root crops at Root times

Radishes, swedes, sugar beet, beetroot, celeriac, carrot, scorzonera, etc., fall into the category of root plants. Potatoes and onions are included in this group too. Root times produce good yields and top storage quality for these crops. Green manure crops are best sown at Root times.

Leaf plants at Leaf times

The cabbage family, lettuce, spinach, lambs lettuce, endive, parsley, leafy herbs and fodder plants are categorised as leaf plants. Leaf times are suitable for sowing and tending these plants but not for harvesting and storage. For this (as well as harvesting of cabbage for sauerkraut) Fruit and Flower times are recommended.

Flower plants at Flower times

These times are favourable for sowing and tending all kinds of flower plants but also for cultivating and spraying 501 (a biodynamic preparation) on oil-bearing plants such as linseed, rape, sunflower, etc. Cut flowers have the strongest scent and remain fresh for longer if cut at Flower times, and the mother plant will provide many new side shoots. If flowers for drying are harvested at Flower times they retain the most vivid colours. If cut at other times they soon lose their colour. Oil-bearing plants are best harvested at Flower times.

Fruit Plants at Fruit times

Plants that are cultivated for their fruit or seed belong to this category, including beans, peas, lentils, soya, maize, tomatoes, cucumber, pumpkin, courgette, but also cereals for summer and winter crops. Sowing oil-bearing plants at Fruit times provides the best yields of seeds. The best time for extraction of oil later on is at Flower times. Leo times are particularly suitable to grow good seed. Fruit plants are best harvested at Fruit times. They store well and their seeds provide good plants for next year. When storing fruit, also remember to choose the time of the ascending Moon.

There is always uncertainty as to which category some plants belong (see list opposite). Onions and beetroot provide a similar yield when sown at Root and Leaf times, but the keeping quality is best from Root times. Broccoli is more beautiful and firmer when sown at Flower times.

Types of crop

Flower plants

artichoke
broccoli
flower bulbs
flowering ornamental shrubs
flowers
flowery herbs
rose
sunflower

Leaf plants

asparagus
Brussels sprouts
cabbage
cauliflower
celery
chard
chicory (endive)
Chinese cabbage (pe-tsai)
corn salad (lamb's lettuce)
crisphead (iceberg) lettuce
curly kale (green cabbage)
endive (chicory)
finocchio (Florence fennel)
green cabbage (curly kale)
iceberg (crisphead) lettuce
kohlrabi
lamb's lettuce (corn salad)
leaf herbs
leek
lettuce
pe-tsai (Chinese cabbage)
red cabbage
rhubarb
shallots
spinach

Root plants

beetroot
black (Spanish) salsify
carrot
celeriac
garlic
green manure crops
horseradish
Jerusalem artichoke
parsnip
potato
radish
red radish
root tubers
Spanish (black) salsify

Fruit plants

aubergine (eggplant)
bush bean
courgette (zucchini)
cucumber
eggplant (aubergine)
grains
lentil
maize
melon
paprika
pea
pumpkin (squash)
runner bean
soya
squash (pumpkin)
tomato
zucchini (courgette)

Explanations of the Calendar Pages

Next to the date is the constellation in which the Moon is positioned (or con-stellations, with time of entry into the new one). This is the astronomical con-stellation, not the astrological sign (see page 22). The next column shows solar and lunar events.

A further column shows which element is dominant on that day (this is also useful for beekeepers). Note H is used for warmth (heat). If there is a change during the day, both elements are mentioned.

The vertical green colour band ■ shows Northern Transplanting Time (see next page), and vertical purple band ■ shows Southern Transplanting Time.

The next column shows in colour the part of the plant which will be en-hanced by sowing or cultivation on that day. Numbers indicate times of day. The column of special events in nature (like storms, thunderstorms, etc.) is being discontinued as weather patterns seem to be changing, and earthquakes and volcanic tendencies are of little help for gardening or agricultural activities.

When parts of the plant are indicated that do not correspond to the Moon's position in the zodiac (often it is more than one part on the same day), it is not a misprint, but takes account of other cosmic aspects (for instance, the Moon's Apogee or trines) which overrule the Moon-zodiac pattern and have an effect on a different part of the plant.

Unfavourable times are marked thus ▬▬▬. These are caused by eclipses, nodal points of the Moon or the planets or other aspects with a negative influ-ence; they are not elaborated upon in the calendar. If one has to sow at unfavour-able times for practical reasons, one can choose favourable times for hoeing, which will improve the plant.

The *position of the planets* in the zodiac is shown in the box below, with the date of entry into a new constellation. R indicates the planet is moving retro-grade (with the date when retrograde begins), D indicates the date when it moves in direct motion again.

On the opposite calendar page astronomical aspects are indicated. Those vis-ible to the naked eye are shown in **bold** type. Visible conjunctions (particularly Mercury's) are not always visible from all parts of the Earth, because the planets may be too close to the horizon in highter latitudes.

Astronomical symbols

Constellations	Planets	Aspects	
♓ Pisces	☉ Sun	☊ Ascending node	E Earth element
♈ Aries	☽ Moon	☋ Descending node	L Light/air element
♉ Taurus	☿ Mercury	⌢ Highest Moon	W Water element
♊ Gemini	♀ Venus	⌣ Lowest Moon	H Warmth (heat)
♋ Cancer	♂ Mars	Pg Perigee	
♌ Leo	♃ Jupiter	Ag Apogee	
♍ Virgo	♄ Saturn	☍ Opposition	▮ Northern Trans-planting Time
♎ Libra	♅ Uranus	☌ Conjunction	
♏ Scorpio	♆ Neptune	⬩ Eclipse/occultation	
♐ Sagittarius	♇ Pluto	⬥ Lunar eclipse	▮ Southern Trans-planting Time
♑ Capricorn	○ Full Moon	△ Trine (or ▲)	
♒ Aquarius	● New Moon		

Transplanting times

From midwinter through to midsummer the Sun rises earlier and sets later each day while its path across the sky ascends higher and higher. From midsummer until midwinter this is reversed, the days get shorter and the midday Sun shines from an ever lower point in the sky. This annual ascending and descending of the Sun creates our seasons. As it ascends and descends during the course of the year, the Sun is slowly moving (from an Earth-centred point of view) through each of the twelve constellations of the zodiac in turn. On average it shines for one month from each constellation.

In the northern hemisphere the winter solstice occurs when the Sun is in the constellation of Sagittarius and the summer solstice when it is in Gemini. At any point from Sagittarius to Gemini the Sun is ascending, while from Gemini to Sagittarius it is descending. In the southern hemisphere this is reversed.

The Moon (and all the planets) follow approximately the same path as the Sun around the zodiac but instead of a year, the Moon takes only about 27½ days to complete one cycle, shining from each constellation in turn for a period of two to three days. This means that the Moon will ascend for about fourteen days and then descend.

It is important to distinguish the journey of the Moon through the zodiac

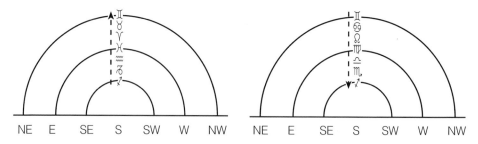

Northern hemisphere ascending Moon (left) and descending Moon (right): Transplanting Time

(siderial rhythm) from the waxing and waning (synodic) cycle: in any given constellation there may be a waxing, waning, full, quarter, sickle or gibbous Moon. As it moves through the zodiac the Moon, like the Sun, is ascending (in the northern hemisphere) when it is in the constellations from Sagittarius to Gemini and descending from Gemini to Sagittarius. In the southern hemisphere it is ascending from Gemini to Sagittarius and descending from Sagittarius to Gemini.

When the Moon is ascending, plant sap rises more strongly. The upper part of the plant fills with sap and vitality. This is a good time for cutting scions (for grafting). Fruit harvested during this period remains fresh for longer when stored.

When the Moon is descending, plants take root readily and connect well with their new location. This period is referred to as the **Transplanting Time**. Moving plants from one location to another is called transplanting. This is the case when young plants are moved from the seedbed into their final growing position but also when the gardener wishes to strengthen the root development of young fruit trees, shrubs or pot plants by frequently re-potting them. Sap movement is slower during the descending Moon. This is why it is a good time for trimming hedges, pruning trees and felling timber as well as applying compost to meadows, pastures and orchards.

Note that sowing is the moment when a seed is put into the soil; either the ascending or descending period can be used. It then needs time to germinate and grow. This is different from *transplanting*, which is best done during the descending Moon. These times are given in the calendar.

Northern Transplanting Times refer to the northern hemisphere, and **Southern Transplanting Times** refer to the southern hemisphere. All other constellations and planetary aspects are equally valid in both hemispheres.

Converting to local time

Times given are Greenwich Mean Time (GMT), using 24-hour clock with ^{h} after the time. Thus 15^h is 3 pm. **No account is taken of daylight saving (summer) time (DST).** Note 0^h is midnight at the beginning of a date, and 24^h is midnight at the end of the date.

Add (+) or subtract (–) times as below. For countries not listed check local time against GMT.

Europe

Britain, Ireland, Portugal: GMT
  (DST March 28 to Oct 30, $+1^h$)
Iceland: GMT (no DST)
Central Europe: $+1^h$
  (DST March 28 to Oct 30, $+2^h$)
Eastern Europe (Finland, etc.): $+2^h$
  (DST March 28 to Oct 30, $+3^h$)
Russia (Moscow): $+3^h$ (no DST)
Georgia: $+4^h$ (no DST)

Africa/Asia

South Africa, Namibia: $+2^h$ (no DST)
Kenya: add 3^h (no DST)
Egypt: add 2^h (no DST)
Israel: add 2^h (DST March 26 to Oct 30, $+3^h$)
India: add $5\frac{1}{2}^h$ (no DST)
Philippines, China: add 8^h (no DST)
Japan, Korea: add 9^h (no DST)

Australia/New Zealand

Western Australia: $+8^h$ (no DST)
Northern Territory: $+9\frac{1}{2}^h$ (no DST)
South Australia: $+9\frac{1}{2}^h$ (DST to April 3 and from Oct 3, $+10\frac{1}{2}^h$)
Queensland: $+10^h$ (no DST)
ACT, NSW, Victoria, Tasmania: $+10^h$
  (DST to April 3 & from Oct 3, $+11^h$)
New Zealand: $+12^h$ (DST to April 3 and from Sep 26, $+13^h$)

North America

Newfoundland Standard Time: $-3\frac{1}{2}^h$
  (DST March 14 to Nov 6, $-2\frac{1}{2}^h$)
Atlantic Standard Time: -4^h
  (DST March 14 to Nov 6, -3^h)
Eastern Standard Time: -5^h
  (DST March 14 to Nov 6, -4^h)
Central Standard Time: -6^h
  (DST March 14 to Nov 6, -5^h, except Saskatchewan with no DST)
Mountain Standard Time: -7^h (DST March 14 to Nov 6, -6^h, except AZ with no DST)
Pacific Standard Time: -8^h
  (DST March 14 to Nov 6, -7^h)
Alaska Standard Time: -9^h
  (DST March 14 to Nov 6, -8^h)
Hawaii Standard Time: -10^h (no DST)
Mexico (mostly CST): -6^h
  (DST April 4 to Oct 30, -5^h)

South America

Argentina: -3^h (no DST)
Brazil (Brasilia): -3^h (no DST)
Chile: -4^h (DST to April 3 and from Sep 5, -3^h)
Columbia, Peru: -5^h (no DST)

January 2021

All times in GMT

Date	Const. of Moon	Solar & lunar aspects	Moon Trines	El'ment	Parts of the plant enhanced by Moon or planets

Northern Tr Time

- 1 Fri ♋ ☉-♐ — W — Leaf
- 2 Sat ♋♌ 6ʰ — W/H — Leaf to 5ʰ / Fruit from 6ʰ

- 3 Sun ♌ — H — Fruit
- 4 Mon ♌♍ 19ʰ — H/E — Fruit to 18ʰ / Root 19ʰ
- 5 Tue ♍ — E — Root
- 6 Wed ♍ ☾ 10ʰ — E — Root
- 7 Thu ♍ — E — Root
- 8 Fri ♍♎ 2ʰ — E/L — 1ʰ / Flower from 2ʰ
- 9 Sat ♎♏ 8ʰ Pg 16ʰ ▲ L/W — Fl -3ʰ

Southern Transplanting Time

- 10 Sun ♏ ☊ 20ʰ — W — Leaf from 5ʰ to 15ʰ
- 11 Mon ♏♐ 12ʰ — W/H — Leaf from 0ʰ to 11ʰ / Fruit from 12ʰ
- 12 Tue ♐ ☋ 8ʰ — H — Fruit
- 13 Wed ♐♑ 15ʰ ● 5ʰ — H/E — Fruit to 14ʰ / 15-17 / Fruit from 18ʰ
- 14 Thu ♑ ▲ E — Fr -3ʰ / Root from 4ʰ
- 15 Fri ♑♒ 17ʰ — E/L — Rt -3ʰ
- 16 Sat ♒ ♀☋ L

- 17 Sun ♒♓ 16ʰ — L/W — Flower from 1ʰ to 15ʰ / Leaf from 16ʰ
- 18 Mon ♓ ☉-♑ — W — Leaf
- 19 Tue ♓ — W — Leaf
- 20 Wed ♓♈ 19ʰ ☽ 21ʰ — W/H — Leaf to 18ʰ / Fruit 19ʰ
- 21 Thu ♈ Ag 13ʰ — H — Fruit
- 22 Fri ♈♉ 19ʰ — H/E — Fruit to 18ʰ / Root 19ʰ
- 23 Sat ♉ — E — Root to 9ʰ

Northern Tr Time

- 24 Sun ♉ ♌ 22ʰ ☿♌ E —
- 25 Mon ♉♊ 19ʰ — E/L — Root from 2ʰ to 18ʰ / Flower 19ʰ
- 26 Tue ♊ ⌒ 15ʰ — L — Flower
- 27 Wed ♊♋ 23ʰ — L/W — Flower to 22ʰ / 23
- 28 Thu ♋ ○ 19ʰ — W — Leaf
- 29 Fri ♋♌ 13ʰ — W/H — Leaf to 12ʰ / Fruit from 13ʰ
- 30 Sat ♌ — H — Fruit

- 31 Sun ♌ — H — Fruit to 24ʰ

0 1 2 3 4 5 6 7 8 9 10 11 12 13 14 15 16 17 18 19 20 21 22 23 24

Mercury ☿	Venus ♀	Mars ♂	Jupiter ♃	Saturn ♄	Uranus ♅	Neptune ♆	Pluto ♇
♐ 7 ♑	♏ 7 ♐	♓	♑	♑	♈	♒	♐
(R 30)	31 ♑	6 ♈			(R 14 D)		

NB: All zodiac symbols refer to astronomical constellations, not astrological signs (see p. 24)

Planetary aspects
(**Bold** = visible to naked eye)

1	☽☍♃ 0ʰ
2	
3	
4	☽☍♆ 10ʰ
5	☿☌♇ 1ʰ
6	
7	☽☍♂ 9ʰ ☽☍⊕ 20ʰ
8	
9	♀△♂ 16ʰ
10	☿☌♄ 3ʰ
11	☿☌♃ 17ʰ ☽☌♀ 20ʰ
12	
13	☽☌♇ 7ʰ ☽☌♄ 22ʰ
14	♀△⊕ 0ʰ ☽☌♃ 3ʰ ☽☌☿ 9ʰ ☉☌♇ 14ʰ
15	
16	♀☍ 12ʰ
17	☽☌♆ 10ʰ
18	
19	
20	♂☌⊕ 21ʰ
21	☽☌⊕ 9ʰ ☽☌♂ 9ʰ
22	
23	
24	☉☌♄ 3ʰ ☿☊ 10ʰ
25	
26	
27	☽☍♀ 16ʰ ☽☍♇ 18ʰ
28	☽☍♄ 12ʰ ♀☌♇ 16ʰ ☽☍♃ 20ʰ
29	☉☌♃ 2ʰ
30	☽☍☿ 2ʰ
31	☽☍♆ 17ʰ

Planet (naked eye) visibility
Evening: Mercury (from 12th), Mars, Jupiter (to 16th), Saturn (to 9th)
All night: -
Morning: Venus (to 31st)

January 2021

With Uranus and Pluto in Warmth constellations, joined by Venus and Mars (from Jan 6–7), together with two Warmth trines, the start of the year is likely to be mild. After the first week, when Mercury joins Jupiter and Saturn in Capricorn, it may become a little cooler.

Northern Transplanting Time
Dec 30 to Jan 12 6ʰ and
Jan 26 17ʰ to Feb 8
Southern Transplanting Time
Jan 12 10ʰ to Jan 26 13ʰ

The transplanting time is a good time for **pruning fruit trees, vines and hedges.** Fruit and Flower times are preferred for this work. Avoid unfavourable times.

Southern hemisphere harvest time for seeds
Always avoid unfavourable times.
Fruit seeds: Jan 2 6ʰ to Jan 4 18ʰ and at other Fruit times.
Flower seeds: Jan 25 19ʰ to Jan 27 22ʰ and other Flower times.
Leaf seeds: Jan 17 16ʰ to Jan 20 18ʰ and other Leaf times.
Root seeds: Jan 4 19ʰ to Jan 8 1ʰ and other Root times.

Control slugs from Dec 31 15ʰ to Jan 2 5ʰ and Jan 27 23ʰ to Jan 29 12ʰ.

When **milk processing** it is best to avoid unfavourable times. This applies to both butter and cheese making. Milk which has been produced at Warmth/Fruit times yields the highest butterfat content. This is also the case on days with a tendency for thunderstorms. Times of perigee (**Pg**) are almost always unfavourable for milk processing and even yoghurt will not turn out well. Starter cultures from such days decay rapidly and it is advisable to produce double the amount the day before. Milk loves Light and Warmth times best of all. Water times are unsuitable.

February 2021

All times in GMT

Date	Const. of Moon	Solar & lunar aspects	Moon Trines El'ment	Parts of the plant enhanced by Moon or planets

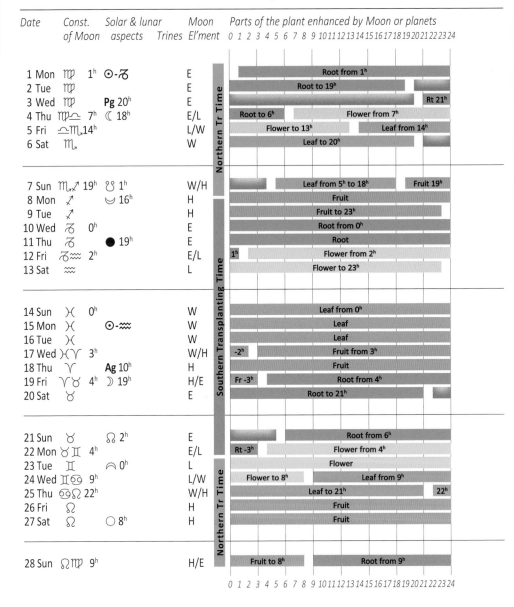

1 Mon ♍ 1ʰ ☉-♑ — E — Root from 1ʰ
2 Tue ♍ — E — Root to 19ʰ
3 Wed ♍ **Pg** 20ʰ — E — Rt 21ʰ
4 Thu ♍♎ 7ʰ ☽ 18ʰ — E/L — Root to 6ʰ — Flower from 7ʰ
5 Fri ♎♏ 14ʰ — L/W — Flower to 13ʰ — Leaf from 14ʰ
6 Sat ♏ — W — Leaf to 20ʰ

7 Sun ♏♐ 19ʰ ☊ 1ʰ — W/H — Leaf from 5ʰ to 18ʰ — Fruit 19ʰ
8 Mon ♐ ☋ 16ʰ — H — Fruit
9 Tue ♐ — H — Fruit to 23ʰ
10 Wed ♑ 0ʰ — E — Root from 0ʰ
11 Thu ♑ ● 19ʰ — E — Root
12 Fri ♑♒ 2ʰ — E/L — 1ʰ Flower from 2ʰ
13 Sat ♒ — L — Flower to 23ʰ

14 Sun ♓ 0ʰ — W — Leaf from 0ʰ
15 Mon ♓ ☉-♒ — W — Leaf
16 Tue ♓ — W — Leaf
17 Wed ♓♈ 3ʰ — W/H — -2ʰ Fruit from 3ʰ
18 Thu ♈ **Ag** 10ʰ — H — Fruit
19 Fri ♈♉ 4ʰ ☽ 19ʰ — H/E — Fr -3ʰ Root from 4ʰ
20 Sat ♉ — E — Root to 21ʰ

21 Sun ♉ ♌ 2ʰ — E — Root from 6ʰ
22 Mon ♉♊ 4ʰ — E/L — Rt -3ʰ Flower from 4ʰ
23 Tue ♊ ♎ 0ʰ — L — Flower
24 Wed ♊♋ 9ʰ — L/W — Flower to 8ʰ — Leaf from 9ʰ
25 Thu ♋♌ 22ʰ — W/H — Leaf to 21ʰ — 22ʰ
26 Fri ♌ — H — Fruit
27 Sat ♌ ○ 8ʰ — H — Fruit

28 Sun ♌♍ 9ʰ — H/E — Fruit to 8ʰ — Root from 9ʰ

Vertical labels: Northern Tr Time — Southern Transplanting Time — Northern Tr Time

0 1 2 3 4 5 6 7 8 9 10 11 12 13 14 15 16 17 18 19 20 21 22 23 24

Mercury ☿	Venus ♀	Mars ♂	Jupiter ♃	Saturn ♄	Uranus ♅	Neptune ♆	Pluto ♇
♑	♑	♈	♑	♑	♈	♒	♐
(R 21 D)	22 ♒	21 ♉					

NB: All zodiac symbols refer to astronomical constellations, not astrological signs (see p. 24)

Planetary aspects
(**Bold** = visible to naked eye)

1
2
3
4   ☾☍⚵ 2^h ☾☌♂ 15^h
5
6   ♀☌♄ 7^h

7
8   ☉☌☿ 14^h
9   ☾☌♇ 17^h
10   ☾☌♄ 13^h ☾☌♀ 22^h ☾☌♃ 23^h
11   ☾☌☿ 7^h ♀☌♃ 15^h
12
13   ☿☌♀ 8^h ☽☌♆ 20^h

14   ☿☌♃ 22^h
15
16
17   ☽☌⚵ 18^h
18
19   ☽☌♂ 1^h
20

21
22
23
24   ☽☍♇ 5^h
25   ♂△♇ 2^h ☽☍♄ 3^h ☽☍☿ 10^h ☽☍♃ 17^h
26   ☽☍♀ 20^h
27

28   ☾☍♆ 3^h

Planet (naked eye) visibility
Evening: Mercury (to 2nd), Mars
All night: -
Morning: -

February 2021

Mercury, Venus, Jupiter and Saturn together with the Sun in the first half of the month are all in Capricorn bringing cold. Mars (until Feb 21), Uranus and Pluto are in Warmth constellations which may counteract this. Only Neptune mediates some Light qualities.

Northern Transplanting Time
Jan 26 to Feb 8 14^h and
Feb 23 2^h to March 7
Southern Transplanting Time
Feb 8 18^h to Feb 22 22^h

Vines, fruit trees and shrubs can be pruned during Transplanting Time selecting Flower and Fruit times in preference. Avoid unfavourable times.

Best times for taking **willow cuttings for hedges and fences:** At Flower times outside Transplanting Time. In warm areas at Flower times during Transplanting Time to avoid too strong a sap current.

Southern hemisphere harvest time for seeds
Always avoid unfavourable times.
Fruit seeds: Feb 7 19^h to Feb 9 23^h, and at other Fruit times.
Flower seeds: Feb 12 2^h to Feb 13 23^h, and at other Flower times.

Control slugs from Feb 24 9^h to Feb 25 21^h.

March 2021

Date	Const. of Moon	Solar & lunar aspects	Trines	Moon El'ment	Parts of the plant enhanced by Moon or planets

March

Date	Const. of Moon	Solar & lunar aspects	Trines	Moon El'ment
1 Mon	♍	☉-♒		E
2 Tue	♍	**Pg** 5ʰ		E
3 Wed	♍♎ 13ʰ		☿ ☋	E/L
4 Thu	♎♏ 19ʰ			L/W
5 Fri	♏			W
6 Sat	♏	☋ 1ʰ ☾ 2ʰ		W
7 Sun	♐	1ʰ ☋ 21ʰ		H
8 Mon	♐			H
9 Tue	♐♑ 6ʰ			H/E
10 Wed	♑			E
11 Thu	♑♒ 9ʰ			E/L
12 Fri	♒	☉-♓		L
13 Sat	♒♓ 8ʰ	● 10ʰ		L/W
14 Sun	♓			W
15 Mon	♓			W
16 Tue	♓♈ 11ʰ			W/H
17 Wed	♈			H
18 Thu	♈♉ 11ʰ	**Ag** 5ʰ		H/E
19 Fri	♉			E
20 Sat	♉	♌ 4ʰ		E
21 Sun	♉♊ 12ʰ	☽ 15ʰ		E/L
22 Mon	♊	⌢ 9ʰ	▲	L
23 Tue	♊♋ 18ʰ			L/W
24 Wed	♋			W
25 Thu	♋♌ 8ʰ			W/H
26 Fri	♌			H
27 Sat	♌♍ 20ʰ			H/E
28 Sun	♍	○ 19ʰ		E
29 Mon	♍			E
30 Tue	♍♎ 22ʰ	**Pg** 6ʰ		E/L
31 Wed	♎			L

DST begins in North America (between 13 and 14)

*DST begins in Europe (incl UK). **All times below continue in GMT*** (between 27 and 28)

Northern Tr Time (1–6)
Southern Transplanting Time (7–20)
Northern Tr Time (21–31)

Parts of the plant enhanced labels:
- Root to 16ʰ (1)
- (2)
- Flower from 6ʰ to 18ʰ — Leaf 19ʰ (3)
- Leaf to 20ʰ (4)
- Leaf from 5ʰ to 24ʰ (5/6)
- Fruit from 1ʰ (7)
- Fruit (8)
- Fruit to 5ʰ — Root from 6ʰ (9)
- Root (10)
- Root to 8ʰ — Flower from 9ʰ (11)
- Flower (12)
- Flower to 7ʰ — Leaf from 8ʰ (13)
- Leaf (14)
- Leaf (15)
- Leaf to 10ʰ — Fruit from 11ʰ (16)
- Fruit (17)
- Fruit to 10ʰ — Root from 11ʰ (18)
- Root to 23ʰ (19)
- Root from 8ʰ (20)
- Root to 11ʰ — 12-14 — Root from 15ʰ (21)
- Root to 6ʰ — Flower from 7ʰ (22)
- Flower to 17ʰ — Leaf from 18ʰ (23)
- Leaf (24)
- Leaf to 7ʰ — Fruit from 8ʰ (25)
- Fruit (26)
- Fruit to 19ʰ — Root 20ʰ (27)
- Root (28)
- Root to 17ʰ (29)
- 19-21 — 22ʰ (30)
- Flower (31)

0 1 2 3 4 5 6 7 8 9 10 11 12 13 14 15 16 17 18 19 20 21 22 23 24

Mercury ☿	Venus ♀	Mars ♂	Jupiter ♃	Saturn ♄	Uranus ⛢	Neptune ♆	Pluto ♇
♑ 13 ♒	♒	♉	♑	♑	♈	♒	♐
30 ♓	14 ♓						

NB: All zodiac symbols refer to astronomical constellations, not astrological signs (see p. 24)

Planetary aspects
*(**Bold** = visible to naked eye)*

March 2021

1	
2	
3	☾ ⚹ ☍ ☋ 9ʰ ☿ ☋ 17ʰ
4	
5	☾ ⚹ ♂ 0ʰ ☿ ☌ ♃ 3ʰ
6	

7	
8	
9	☾ ☌ ♇ 1ʰ
10	**☾ ☌ ♄ 1ʰ ☾ ☌ ♃ 18ʰ**
11	☉ ☌ ♆ 0ʰ ☾ ☌ ☿ 4ʰ
12	
13	☾ ☌ ♀ 4ʰ ☾ ☌ ♆ 6ʰ

14	♀ ☌ ♆ 4ʰ
15	
16	
17	☽ ☌ ☋ 4ʰ
18	
19	☽ ☌ ♂ 18ʰ
20	

21	
22	♂ △ ♄ 3ʰ
23	☽ ⚹ ♇ 15ʰ
24	☽ ⚹ ♄ 18ʰ
25	☽ ⚹ ♃ 13ʰ
26	☉ ☌ ♀ 8ʰ
27	☽ ⚹ ☿ 8ʰ ☽ ⚹ ♆ 15ʰ

28	☾ ⚹ ♀ 20ʰ
29	
30	☿ ☌ ♆ 3ʰ ☾ ⚹ ☋ 20ʰ
31	

In the first half Venus and in the second half of the month Mercury are in Aquarius, bringing Light, aided by Neptune. Mars, Jupiter and Saturn are in Earth constellations bringing cooler influences that are counteracted to some extent by Uranus and Pluto in Warmth constellations.

Northern Transplanting Time
Feb 23 to March 7 19ʰ and
March 22 11ʰ to April 3
Southern Transplanting Time
March 7 23ʰ to March 22 7ʰ

Willow cuttings for **pollen production** are best cut from March 22 11ʰ to March 23 17ʰ; and for **honey flow** from March 25 8ʰ to March 27 19ʰ. Avoid unfavourable times.

Cuttings for grafting: Cut outside Transplanting Time during ascending Moon – always choosing times (Fruit, Leaf, etc.) according to the part of plant to be enhanced.

Control slugs: March 23 18ʰ to March 25 7ʰ.

Southern hemisphere harvest time for seeds
Always avoid unfavourable times.
Fruit seeds: March 25 8ʰ to March 27 19ʰ, and at other Fruit times.
Flower seeds: Flower times.
Leaf seeds: Leaf times.
Root seeds: Root times.

Biodynamic preparations
Pick dandelion in March or April in the mornings during Flower times. The flowers should not be quite open in the centre. Dry them on paper in the shade, not in bright sunlight. Once dried they can be stored until suitably encased and buried in the ground.

Planet (naked eye) visibility
Evening: Mars
All night: -
Morning: Jupiter (from 1st), Saturn (from 4th)

Unfavourable time

April 2021

Date	Const. of Moon	Solar & lunar aspects	Trines	Moon El'ment	Parts of the plant enhanced by Moon or planets

April

1 Thu ♎︎♏︎ 3ʰ ☉-♓︎ — L/W — NTT
2 Fri ♏︎ Good Friday ☍3ʰ — W
3 Sat ♏︎♐︎ 6ʰ — W/H
DST ends in Australia and New Zealand

4 Sun ♐︎ Easter ☋2ʰ ☾10ʰ — H
5 Mon ♐︎♑︎ 11ʰ — H/E
6 Tue ♑︎ — E
7 Wed ♑︎♒︎ 15ʰ — E/L
8 Thu ♒︎ — L
9 Fri ♒︎♓︎ 14ʰ — L/W
10 Sat ♓︎ — W

11 Sun ♓︎ — W
12 Mon ♓︎♈︎ 18ʰ ● 3ʰ — W/H
13 Tue ♈︎ — H
14 Wed ♈︎♉︎ 18ʰ **Ag** 18ʰ — H/E
15 Thu ♉︎ — E
16 Fri ♉︎ ☍ 6ʰ — E
17 Sat ♉︎♊︎ 19ʰ ▲ ●♂︎ — E/L

18 Sun ♊︎ ⚲ 16ʰ — L
19 Mon ♊︎ ☉-♈︎ — L
20 Tue ♊︎♋︎ 2ʰ ☽ 7ʰ — L/W
21 Wed ♋︎♌︎ 17ʰ — W/H
22 Thu ♌︎ ☿☍ — H
23 Fri ♌︎ — H
24 Sat ♌︎♍︎ 6ʰ — H/E

25 Sun ♍︎ — E
26 Mon ♍︎ — E
27 Tue ♍︎♎︎ 8ʰ ○ 4ʰ **Pg** 15ʰ — E/L
28 Wed ♎︎♏︎ 13ʰ — L/W
29 Thu ♏︎ ☍ 9ʰ — W
30 Fri ♏︎♐︎ 15ʰ — W/H

Southern Transplanting Time
Northern Transplanting Time

	Mercury ☿	Venus ♀	Mars ♂	Jupiter ♃	Saturn ♄	Uranus ♅	Neptune ♆	Pluto ♇
	♓︎ 19 ♈︎	♓︎	♉︎	♑︎	♑︎	♈︎	♒︎	♐︎
	30 ♉︎	14 ♈︎	22 ♊︎	20 ♒︎			7 ♓︎	(27 R)

NB: All zodiac symbols refer to astronomical constellations, not astrological signs (see p. 24)

Planetary aspects
(**Bold** = visible to naked eye)

April 2021

1
2 ☾ ☌ ♂ 11ʰ
3

4
5 ☾ ☌ ♇ 7ʰ
6 **☾ ☌ ♄ 11ʰ**
7 **☾ ☌ ♃ 10ʰ**
8
9 ☾ ☌ ♆ 14ʰ
10

11 ☾ ☌ ☿ 9ʰ
12 ☽ ☌ ♀ 12ʰ
13 ☽ ☌ ⊕ 13ʰ
14
15
16
17 ♂ △ ♃ 5ʰ ☽ ☍ ♂ 12ʰ

18
19 ☉ ☌ ☿ 2ʰ
20 ☽ ☍ ♇ 0ʰ
21 ☽ ☍ ♄ 6ʰ
22 ☽ ☍ ♃ 8ʰ ☿ Ω 9ʰ
23 ♀ ☌ ⊕ 1ʰ
24 ☽ ☍ ♆ 3ʰ ☿ ☌ ⊕ 7ʰ

25 ☿ ☌ ♀ 22ʰ
26
27 ☾ ☍ ⊕ 9ʰ ☾ ☍ ♀ 18ʰ ☾ ☍ ☿ 20ʰ
28
29
30 ☉ ☌ ⊕ 20ʰ

In the first half of the month Mercury and Venus in Pisces, joined by Neptune on April 7, may bring precipitation. Until April 20–22 Mars, Jupiter and Saturn in Earth constellations bring cold, to some extent balanced by Uranus and Pluto in Warmth constellations.

Northern Transplanting Time
March 22 to April 3 24ʰ and
April 18 18ʰ to May 1
Southern Transplanting Time
April 4 4ʰ to April 18 14ʰ

The **soil warms up** on April 19.

Grafting of fruiting shrubs at Fruit times outside transplanting times.
  Grafting of flowering shrubs at Flower times outside transplanting times.

Control
Slugs from April 20 2ʰ to April 21 16ʰ.
Clothes and wax moths from April 9 14ʰ to April 12 17ʰ.

Southern hemisphere harvest time for seeds
Always avoid unfavourable times.
Fruit seeds: Specially good from April 22 22ʰ to April 24 5ʰ and at other Fruit times.
Flower seeds April 7 15ʰ to April 9 13ʰ, and other at Flower times.
Leaf seeds at Leaf times, and **Root seeds** at Root times.

Biodynamic preparations
The preparations can be taken out of the ground after April 28 avoiding unfavourable times (best at Fruit or Flower times). Preparations put into the ground after Sep 15, 2020, should wait to the end of May.

Planet (naked eye) visibility
Evening: Mercury (from 29th), Venus (from 20th), Mars
All night: -
Morning: Jupiter, Saturn

Unfavourable time

May

Date	Const. of Moon	Solar & lunar aspects	Trines	Moon El'ment	Parts of the plant enhanced by Moon or planets

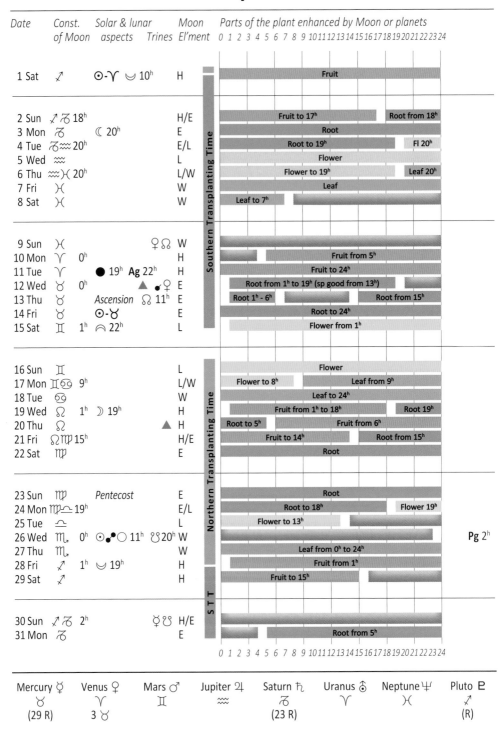

Parts of the plant enhanced by Moon or planets — scale 0 1 2 3 4 5 6 7 8 9 10 11 12 13 14 15 16 17 18 19 20 21 22 23 24

Southern Transplanting Time

- 1 Sat ♐ — ☉-♈ �!10ʰ — H — Fruit
- 2 Sun ♐♑18ʰ — H/E — Fruit to 17ʰ · Root from 18ʰ
- 3 Mon ♑ — ☾20ʰ — E — Root
- 4 Tue ♑≈20ʰ — E/L — Root to 19ʰ · Fl 20ʰ
- 5 Wed ≈ — L — Flower
- 6 Thu ≈⟩(20ʰ — L/W — Flower to 19ʰ · Leaf 20ʰ
- 7 Fri)(— W — Leaf
- 8 Sat)(— W — Leaf to 7ʰ

- 9 Sun)(— ♀♌ — W — Fruit from 5ʰ
- 10 Mon ♈ 0ʰ — H — Fruit from 5ʰ
- 11 Tue ♈ — ● 19ʰ Ag 22ʰ — H — Fruit to 24ʰ
- 12 Wed ♉ 0ʰ — ▲ ●♀ — E — Root from 1ʰ to 19ʰ (sp good from 13ʰ)
- 13 Thu ♉ — Ascension ♌11ʰ — E — Root 1ʰ - 6ʰ · Root from 15ʰ
- 14 Fri ♉ — ☉-♉ — E — Root to 24ʰ
- 15 Sat ♊ 1ʰ ♎22ʰ — L — Flower from 1ʰ

Northern Transplanting Time

- 16 Sun ♊ — L — Flower
- 17 Mon ♊♋ 9ʰ — L/W — Flower to 8ʰ · Leaf from 9ʰ
- 18 Tue ♋ — W — Leaf to 24ʰ
- 19 Wed ♌ 1ʰ ☽19ʰ — H — Fruit from 1ʰ to 18ʰ · Root 19ʰ
- 20 Thu ♌ — ▲ — H — Root to 5ʰ · Fruit from 6ʰ
- 21 Fri ♌♍15ʰ — H/E — Fruit to 14ʰ · Root from 15ʰ
- 22 Sat ♍ — E — Root

- 23 Sun ♍ — Pentecost — E — Root
- 24 Mon ♍♎19ʰ — E/L — Root to 18ʰ · Flower 19ʰ
- 25 Tue ♎ — L — Flower to 13ʰ
- 26 Wed ♏ 0ʰ — ☉●○11ʰ ℧20ʰ — W — Pg 2ʰ
- 27 Thu ♏ — W — Leaf from 0ʰ to 24ʰ
- 28 Fri ♐ 1ʰ �!19ʰ — H — Fruit from 1ʰ
- 29 Sat ♐ — H — Fruit to 15ʰ

STT

- 30 Sun ♐♑ 2ʰ — ☿℧♀ — H/E —
- 31 Mon ♑ — E — Root from 5ʰ

scale 0 1 2 3 4 5 6 7 8 9 10 11 12 13 14 15 16 17 18 19 20 21 22 23 24

Mercury ☿	Venus ♀	Mars ♂	Jupiter ♃	Saturn ♄	Uranus ♅	Neptune ♆	Pluto ♇
♉	♈	♊	≈	♑	♈	)(	♐
(29 R)	3 ♉			(23 R)			(R)

NB: All zodiac symbols refer to astronomical constellations, not astrological signs (see p. 24)

Planetary aspects
*(**Bold** = visible to naked eye)*

May 2021

1	☾☍♂ 0^h
2	☿△♇ 9^h ☾☌♇ 14^h
3	☾☌♄ 19^h
4	
5	☾☌♃ 0^h
6	♀△♇ 11^h ☾☌♆ 21^h
7	
8	
9	♀♌ 16^h
10	☾☌♁ 23^h
11	
12	☿△♄ 19^h ☽☌♀ 22^h
13	☽☌☿ 19^h
14	
15	
16	☽☌♂ 5^h
17	☽☍♇ 6^h ☉△♇ 10^h
18	☽☍♄ 14^h
19	☽☍♃ 22^h
20	♀△♄ 2^h
21	☽☍♆ 13^h
22	
23	
24	☽☍♁ 22^h
25	
26	
27	☾☍♀ 15^h ☾☍☿ 18^h
28	
29	☿☌♀ 5^h ☾☍♂ 15^h ☾☌♇ 22^h
30	☿☊ 16^h
31	☾☌♄ 3^h ♂△♆ 5^h

Mercury, Venus and Saturn in Earth constellations, together with two Earth trines will bring cooler weather. Uranus and Pluto bring Warmth while Mars and Jupiter bring Light influences. Only Neptune in Pisces may bring some rain.

Northern Transplanting Time
April 18 to May 1 8^h and
May 16 0^h to May 28 17^h
Southern Transplanting Time
May 1 12^h to May 15 20^h and
May 28 21^h to June 12

Transplant **table potatoes** at Root times.
Transplant **seed potatoes** for 2022 from May 10 5^h to May 11 23^h.

Hay should be cut between May 15 1^h and May 17 8^h, and at other Flower times.

Control
Moths from May 6 20^h to May 9 23^h.
Flies by burning fly papers in the cow barn at Flower times.
Mole crickets ash from May 26 0^h to May 27 24^h.
Chitinous insects, wheat weevil, Colorado beetle and varroa from May 12 0^h to May 14 24^h.

Begin **queen bee** rearing (grafting or larval transfer, comb insertion, cell punching) between May 15 1^h and May 17 8^h and at other Flower times.

Planet (naked eye) visibility
Evening: Mercury (to 27th), Venus, Mars
All night: -
Morning: Jupiter, Saturn

Unfavourable time

June 2021

Date	Const. of Moon	Solar & lunar aspects	Trines	Moon El'ment	Parts of the plant enhanced by Moon or planets

Date	Const. of Moon	Solar & lunar aspects	Trines	Moon El'ment
1 Tue	♑︎♒︎ 4ʰ	☉-♉︎		E/L
2 Wed	♒︎	☾ 5ʰ		L
3 Thu	♒︎)(2ʰ		▲	L/W
4 Fri	)(		▲	W
5 Sat	)(			W
6 Sun	)(♈︎ 6ʰ			W/H
7 Mon	♈︎			H
8 Tue	♈︎♉︎ 6ʰ	Ag 2ʰ		H/E
9 Wed	♉︎	♌︎ 17ʰ		E
10 Thu	♉︎	☉☌● 11ʰ		E
11 Fri	♉︎♊︎ 7ʰ			E/L
12 Sat	♊︎	⌒ 4ʰ		L
13 Sun	♊︎♋︎ 14ʰ			L/W
14 Mon	♋︎			W
15 Tue	♋︎♌︎ 6ʰ			W/H
16 Wed	♌︎			H
17 Thu	♌︎♍︎ 22ʰ			H/E
18 Fri	♍︎	☽ 4ʰ		E
19 Sat	♍︎			E
20 Sun	♍︎	☉-♊︎		E
21 Mon	♍︎♎︎ 4ʰ			E/L
22 Tue	♎︎♏︎ 10ʰ			L/W
23 Wed	♏︎	♋︎ 6ʰ Pg 10ʰ	▲	W
24 Thu	♏︎♐︎ 11ʰ	○ 19ʰ		W/H
25 Fri	♐︎	☝ 6ʰ		H
26 Sat	♐︎♑︎ 12ʰ			H/E
27 Sun	♑︎			E
28 Mon	♑︎♒︎ 12ʰ			E/L
29 Tue	♒︎			L
30 Wed	♒︎)(10ʰ			L/W

Southern Transplanting Time
Northern Transplanting Time
Southern Tr Time

Mercury ☿	Venus ♀	Mars ♂	Jupiter ♃	Saturn ♄	Uranus ⛢	Neptune ♆	Pluto ♇
♉︎	♉︎ 3 ♊︎	♊︎	♒︎	♑︎	♈︎	)(	♐︎
(R 22 D)	25 ♋︎	7 ♋︎	(20 R)	(R)		(25 R)	(R)

NB: All zodiac symbols refer to astronomical constellations, not astrological signs (see p. 24)

Planetary aspects
*(**Bold** = visible to naked eye)*

1 **☾ ☌ ♃** 12^h
2
3 ☾ ☌ ♅ 5^h **☉ △ ♄** 19^h
4 ♀ ☌ ♃ 0^h
5 ♂ ☍ ♇ 20^h

6
7 ☾ ☌ ♁ 8^h
8
9
10 ☽ ☌ ☿ 13^h
11 ☉ ☌ ☿ 1^h
12 ☽ ☌ ♀ 7^h

13 ☽ ☍ ♇ 11^h ☽ ☌ ♂ 21^h
14 ☽ ☍ ♄ 19^h
15
16 ☽ ☍ ♃ 7^h
17 ☽ ☍ ♅ 21^h
18
19

20
21 ☽ ☍ ♁ 10^h ♀ △ ♅ 14^h
22
23 ☉ △ ♃ 10^h ☽ ☍ ☿ 15^h
24 ♀ ☍ ♇ 0^h
25
26 ☾ ☌ ♇ 8^h ☾ ☍ ♀ 13^h

27 ☾ ☍ ♂ 7^h **☾ ☌ ♄** 11^h
28 **☾ ☌ ♃** 22^h
29
30 ☾ ☌ ♅ 12^h

June 2021

There is a mixed picture for June. There are Warmth, Light and Earth constellations. Pluto and Uranus are in Warmth constellations, while Mercury and Saturn are in Earth constellations, intensifying the cold effect in their retrograde motion. Jupiter and (for most of the month) Venus are in Light constellations, and there are two Light trines. Mars moves into Cancer on June 7, and, together with Neptune in Pisces, may bring precipitation.

Northern Transplanting Time
June 12 6^h to June 25 4^h
Southern Transplanting Time
May 28 to June 12 2^h and
June 25 8^h to July 9

Cut **hay** at Flower times.

Begin **queen bee** rearing at Fruit and Flower times, avoiding unfavourable times.

Control
Chitinous insects, wheat weevil, Colorado beetle and varroa from June 8 6^h to June 11 6^h.
Flies by burning fly papers in the cow barn from June 1 4^h to June 3 1^h, and June 28 12^h to June 30 9^h and at other Flower times.
Grasshoppers from June 11 7^h to June 13 13^h.
Mole crickets ash from June 22 10^h to June 24 10^h.

Maria Thun's biodynamic tree log preparations
Cut **oak** logs, fill them with ground **oak bark** and put them into the earth between June 5 9^h and June 6 2^h.
    Cut **birch** logs, fill with dried **yarrow** and put into the ground between June 23 23^h and June 24 6^h.

June

Planet (naked eye) visibility
Evening: Venus, Mars (to 29th)
All night: -
Morning: Jupiter, Saturn

Unfavourable time

All times in GMT

Date	Const. of Moon	Solar & lunar aspects	Trines	Moon El'ment	Parts of the plant enhanced by Moon or planets

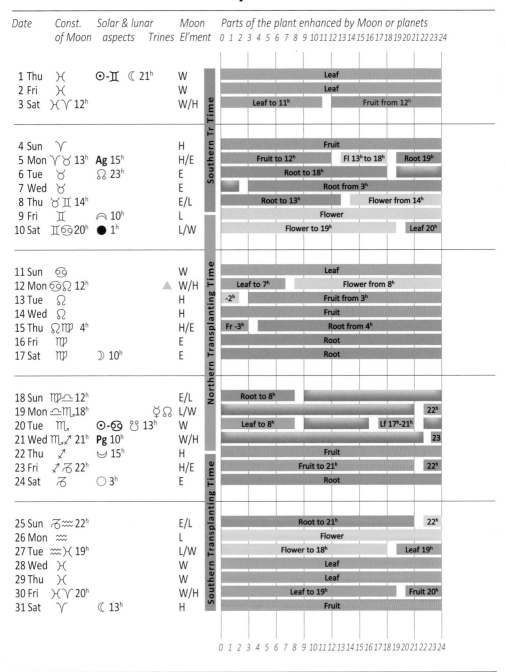

The chart, with a vertical label reading "Southern Tr Time" for the first block, "Northern Transplanting Time" for the middle blocks, and "Southern Transplanting Time" for the last block:

Date	Const. of Moon	Solar & lunar aspects	Trines	Moon El'ment	Parts of the plant
1 Thu	♓	☉-♊ ☾ 21ʰ		W	Leaf
2 Fri	♓			W	Leaf
3 Sat	♓♈ 12ʰ			W/H	Leaf to 11ʰ / Fruit from 12ʰ
4 Sun	♈			H	Fruit
5 Mon	♈♉ 13ʰ	**Ag** 15ʰ		H/E	Fruit to 12ʰ / Fl 13ʰ to 18ʰ / Root 19ʰ
6 Tue	♉	☍ 23ʰ		E	Root to 18ʰ
7 Wed	♉			E	Root from 3ʰ
8 Thu	♉♊ 14ʰ			E/L	Root to 13ʰ / Flower from 14ʰ
9 Fri	♊		⌒ 10ʰ	L	Flower
10 Sat	♊♋ 20ʰ	● 1ʰ		L/W	Flower to 19ʰ / Leaf 20ʰ
11 Sun	♋			W	Leaf
12 Mon	♋♌ 12ʰ		▲	W/H	Leaf to 7ʰ / Flower from 8ʰ
13 Tue	♌			H	-2ʰ / Fruit from 3ʰ
14 Wed	♌			H	Fruit
15 Thu	♌♍ 4ʰ			H/E	Fr -3ʰ / Root from 4ʰ
16 Fri	♍			E	Root
17 Sat	♍	☽ 10ʰ		E	Root
18 Sun	♍♎ 12ʰ			E/L	Root to 8ʰ
19 Mon	♎♏ 18ʰ		☿☍	L/W	22ʰ
20 Tue	♏	☉-♋ ☍ 13ʰ		W	Leaf to 8ʰ / Lf 17ʰ-21ʰ
21 Wed	♏♐ 21ʰ	**Pg** 10ʰ		W/H	23
22 Thu	♐	☋ 15ʰ		H	Fruit
23 Fri	♐♑ 22ʰ			H/E	Fruit to 21ʰ / 22ʰ
24 Sat	♑	○ 3ʰ		E	Root
25 Sun	♑♒ 22ʰ			E/L	Root to 21ʰ / 22ʰ
26 Mon	♒			L	Flower
27 Tue	♒♓ 19ʰ			L/W	Flower to 18ʰ / Leaf 19ʰ
28 Wed	♓			W	Leaf
29 Thu	♓			W	Leaf
30 Fri	♓♈ 20ʰ			W/H	Leaf to 19ʰ / Fruit 20ʰ
31 Sat	♈	☾ 13ʰ		H	Fruit

0 1 2 3 4 5 6 7 8 9 10 11 12 13 14 15 16 17 18 19 20 21 22 23 24

Mercury ☿	Venus ♀	Mars ♂	Jupiter ♃	Saturn ♄	Uranus ♅	Neptune ♆	Pluto ♇
♉ 11 ♊	♋	♋	♒	♑	♈	♓	♐
26 ♋	12 ♌	11 ♌	(R)	(R)		(R)	(R)

NB: All zodiac symbols refer to astronomical constellations, not astrological signs (see p. 24)

Planetary aspects
*(**Bold** = visible to naked eye)*

1 ♂☌♄ 13^h
2
3

4 ☽☌⊕ 17^h
5
6
7 ♀☍♄ 3^h
8 ☽☌☿ 4^h
9
10 ☽☍♇ 16^h

11 ☽☍♄ 23^h
12 **☽☌♀ 11^h** ☽☌♂ 13^h ☿△♃ 20^h
13 ☽☍♃ 11^h ♀☌♂ 14^h
14
15 ☽☍♆ 2^h ☉△♆ 9^h
16
17 ☉☍♇ 23^h

18 ☽☍⊕ 19^h
19 ☿♌ 9^h
20
21
22 ♀☍♃ 13^h
23 ☽☍☿ 8^h ☽☌♇ 17^h
24 ☿△♆ 17^h **☽☌♄ 18^h**

25 ☿☍♇ 20^h **☽☍♂ 23^h**
26 **☽☌♃ 4^h** **☽☍♀ 13^h**
27 **☽☌♆ 21^h**
28
29 ♂☍♃ 16^h
30
31

Planet (naked eye) visibility
Evening: Venus
All night: Jupiter, Saturn
Morning: -

July 2021

In the first half of the month Venus and Mars, (as well as Neptune throughout) are in Water constellations bringing rain. Then they move into Leo; together with Uranus in Aries and Pluto in Sagittarius this will bring warmth.

Northern Transplanting Time
July 9 12^h to July 22 13^h
Southern Transplanting Time
June 25 to July 9 8^h and July 22 17^h to Aug 5

Late hay cut at Flower times.

Summer harvest for seeds:
Flower plants: Harvest at Flower times, specially in the first half of the month.
    Fruit plants from July 13 3^h to July 15 3^h, or at other Fruit times.
    Harvest **leaf plants** at Leaf times.
    Harvest **root plants** at Root times, especially July 5 19^h to July 8 13^h, and July 15 4^h to July 18 8^h. Always avoid unfavourable times.

Control
Flies: burn fly papers in the cow barn at Flower times.
Slugs: burn from July 10 20^h to July 12 11^h. Spray leaf plants and the soil with horn silica early in the morning during Leaf times.
Grasshoppers from July 8 14^h to July 10 19^h.

Maria Thun's biodynamic tree log preparations
Cut **oak** logs, fill with ground **oak bark** and put them into the ground on July 1 between 2^h and 19^h or July 29 between 5^h and 22^h.
    Cut **maple** logs, fill with dried **dandelion** and put them into the ground between July 17 12^h and July 18 5^h.
    Cut **birch** logs, fill with dried **yarrow** and put them into the ground on July 22 between 2^h and 19^h.
    Cut **larch** logs, fill with dried **camomile** and put them into the ground between July 25 9^h and July 26 2^h.

July

August 2021

Date	Const. of Moon	Solar & lunar aspects	Trines	Moon El'ment	Parts of the plant enhanced by Moon or planets

(Parts of the plant enhanced by Moon or planets — graphical chart, hours 0–24)

Northern Transplanting Time / STT

Date	Const. of Moon	Solar & lunar aspects	Trines	Moon El'ment	Plant parts
1 Sun	♈♉ 20ʰ	☉-♋		H/E	Fruit to 19ʰ · 20-22 · 23
2 Mon	♉	**Ag** 8ʰ		E	Flower to 11ʰ · Root from 12ʰ to 22ʰ
3 Tue	♉	♌ 3ʰ	▲	E	Fr 7-10ʰ · Root from 11ʰ
4 Wed	♉♊ 21ʰ			E/L	Root to 20ʰ · Fl 21ʰ
5 Thu	♊	♐ 17ʰ		L	Flower
6 Fri	♊			L	Flower
7 Sat	♊♋ 4ʰ			L/W	Fl -3ʰ · Leaf from 4ʰ
8 Sun	♋♌ 19ʰ	● 14ʰ		W/H	Leaf to 18ʰ · Fruit 19ʰ
9 Mon	♌			H	Fruit
10 Tue	♌			H	Fruit
11 Wed	♌♍ 9ʰ	☉-♌		H/E	Fruit to 8ʰ · Root from 9ʰ
12 Thu	♍			E	Root
13 Fri	♍			E	Root
14 Sat	♍♎ 17ʰ			E/L	Root to 16ʰ · Flower from 17ʰ
15 Sun	♎	☽ 15ʰ		L	Flower to 23ʰ
16 Mon	♏ 0ʰ	☋ 16ʰ		W	Leaf from 0ʰ to 11ʰ
17 Tue	♏	**Pg** 9ʰ		W	22ʰ
18 Wed	♏♐ 4ʰ	☄ 22ʰ		W/H	Lf -3ʰ · Fruit from 4ʰ
19 Thu	♐			H	Fruit
20 Fri	♐♑ 7ʰ		▲	H/E	Fruit to 11ʰ (sp good 2ʰ-6ʰ) · Root from 12ʰ
21 Sat	♑			E	Root to 18ʰ · Fruit 19ʰ
22 Sun	♑♒ 7ʰ	○ 12ʰ	▲	E/L	Fruit to 11ʰ · Flower from 12ʰ
23 Mon	♒		▲	L	Flower to 6ʰ · Root from 7ʰ to 16ʰ · Flower from 17ʰ
24 Tue	♒♓ 4ʰ			L/W	Fl -3ʰ · Leaf from 4ʰ
25 Wed	♓			W	Leaf to 15ʰ
26 Thu	♓	☿☋		W	
27 Fri	♓♈ 4ʰ			W/H	Fruit from 5ʰ to 20ʰ
28 Sat	♈			H	
29 Sun	♈♉ 4ʰ	♀☋		H/E	Flower 18ʰ-24ʰ
30 Mon	♉	**Ag** 2ʰ ♌ 5ʰ ☾ 7ʰ		E	Root from 9ʰ
31 Tue	♉			E	Root

Southern Transplanting Time

Mercury ☿	Venus ♀	Mars ♂	Jupiter ♃	Saturn ♄	Uranus ♅	Neptune ♆	Pluto ♇
♋ 6 ♌	♌	♌	♒ 24 ♑	♑	♈	♓	♐
25 ♍	10 ♍		(R)	(R)	(20 R)	(R)	(R)

NB: All zodiac symbols refer to astronomical constellations, not astrological signs (see p. 24)

Planetary aspects
*(**Bold** = visible to naked eye)*

1	☽ ☌ ⚶ 2^h ☉ ☌ ☿ 14^h ☿ ☍ ♄ 22^h
2	☉ ☍ ♄ 6^h
3	♀ △ ⚶ 7^h
4	
5	
6	☽ ☌ ♇ 22^h
7	
8	☽ ☌ ♄ 2^h
9	☽ ☌ ☿ 6^h ☽ ☍ ♃ 12^h
10	♀ ☍ ♅ 0^h ☽ ☌ ♂ 4^h
11	☿ ☍ ♃ 1^h ☽ ☍ ♅ 7^h ☽ ☌ ♀ 10^h ♀ △ ♇ 23^h
12	
13	
14	
15	☽ ☍ ⚶ 1^h
16	
17	
18	
19	☿ ☌ ♂ 3^h
20	☽ ☌ ♇ 0^h ☉ ☍ ♃ 0^h ☿ △ ⚶ 8^h
21	☽ ☌ ♄ 0^h
22	☽ ☌ ♃ 7^h ♂ △ ⚶ 7^h
23	♀ △ ♄ 13^h ☽ ☌ ♂ 17^h
24	☽ ☍ ☿ 2^h ☽ ☌ ♅ 5^h
25	☿ ☍ ♅ 1^h ☽ ☍ ♀ 16^h
26	☿ △ ♇ 14^h ☿ ⚻ 16^h
27	
28	☽ ☌ ⚶ 10^h
29	♀ ⚻ 5^h
30	
31	

Planet (naked eye) visibility
Evening: Venus
All night: Jupiter, Saturn
Morning: -

August 2021

August is dominated by Warmth constellations, reinforced by three Warmth trines. By the end of the month Mercury, Venus and Jupiter join Saturn in cooler Earth constellations. Only Neptune in Pisces will hopefully bring some rain.

Northern Transplanting Time
Aug 5 19^h to Aug 18 20^h
Southern Transplanting Time
July 22 to Aug 5 15^h and Aug 19 0^h to Sep 1

Harvest **seeds of fruit plants** and **grain** to be used for seed from Aug 8 19^h to Aug 11 8^h, and at other Fruit times, avoiding unfavourable times.

Immediately after harvest, sow catch crops like lupins, phacelia, mustard or wild flax.

Seeds for leaf plants: harvest at Leaf times, specially in the second half of the month.

Seeds for flower plants: at Flower times, specially in the second half of the month.

Burn **fly papers** in the cow barn at Flower times.

Ants in the house: burn when the Moon is in Leo, Aug 8 19^h to Aug 11 8^h.

Biodynamic preparations
Cut **yarrow** in the mornings at Fruit times after Aug 11. The blossoms should show some seed formation.

Maria Thun's biodynamic tree log preparations
Cut **larch** logs, fill with dried **camomile** and put them into the ground between Aug 1 11^h and Aug 2 4^h or between Aug 10 14^h and Aug 11 7^h.

Cut **maple** logs, fill with dried **dandelion** and put them into the ground between Aug 1 19^h and Aug 2 12^h or between Aug 19 13^h and Aug 20 6^h.

Cut **birch** logs, fill with dried **yarrow** (from last year) and put them into the ground between Aug 9 13^h and Aug 10 6^h.

Aug

September 2021

Date	Const. of Moon	Solar & lunar aspects	Trines	Moon El'ment	Parts of the plant enhanced by Moon or planets

Northern Transplanting Time

- 1 Wed ♉Ⅱ 5ʰ ☉-♌ E/L — Root to 4ʰ / Flower from 5ʰ
- 2 Thu Ⅱ ⌒ 0ʰ L — Flower
- 3 Fri Ⅱ♋12ʰ L/W — Flower to 11ʰ / Leaf from 12ʰ
- 4 Sat ♋ W — Leaf to 19ʰ / Root 20ʰ

- 5 Sun ♋♌ 3ʰ ▲ W/H — Root to 5ʰ / Fruit from 6ʰ
- 6 Mon ♌ ▲▲ H — Fr to 8ʰ (sp good) / Root 9ʰ to 16ʰ / Fruit 17ʰ (sp gd)
- 7 Tue ♌♍17ʰ ● 1ʰ ▲ H/E — Fruit to 16ʰ (sp good to 4ʰ) / Root from 17ʰ
- 8 Wed ♍ E — Root
- 9 Thu ♍ E — Root
- 10 Fri ♍♎23ʰ E/L — Root to 21ʰ
- 11 Sat ♎ **Pg** 10ʰ L — 23

- 12 Sun ♎♏ 5ʰ ☍ 17ʰ L/W — Fl to 4ʰ / Leaf 5ʰ to 12ʰ / Lf 21ʰ
- 13 Mon ♏ ☽ 21ʰ W — Leaf
- 14 Tue ♏♐ 10ʰ W/H — Leaf to 9ʰ / Fruit from 10ʰ
- 15 Wed ♐ ☌ 4ʰ H — Fruit
- 16 Thu ♐♑13ʰ ☉-♍ H/E — Fruit to 12ʰ / Root from 13ʰ
- 17 Fri ♑ E — Root
- 18 Sat ♑♒15ʰ E/L — Root to 14ʰ / Flower from 15ʰ

Southern Transplanting Time

- 19 Sun ♒ L — Flower
- 20 Mon ♒♓12ʰ ○ 24ʰ ▲ L/W — Flower to 11ʰ / Lf 12-16ʰ / Root from 17ʰ
- 21 Tue ♓ W — -2ʰ / Leaf from 3ʰ
- 22 Wed ♓ W — Leaf
- 23 Thu ♓♈12ʰ W/H — Leaf to 11ʰ / Fruit from 12ʰ
- 24 Fri ♈ H — Fruit
- 25 Sat ♈♉12ʰ H/E — Fruit to 11ʰ / Root from 12ʰ

DST begins in New Zealand

- 26 Sun ♉ ☍ 8ʰ **Ag** 22ʰ E — Rt -3ʰ / Fruit from 13ʰ
- 27 Mon ♉ E — 1ʰ / Root from 2ʰ
- 28 Tue ♉Ⅱ 13ʰ E/L — Root to 12ʰ / Flower from 13ʰ
- 29 Wed Ⅱ ☾ 2ʰ ⌒ 8ʰ ▲▲ L — Flower to 17ʰ (sp good from 9ʰ) / Root from 18ʰ
- 30 Thu Ⅱ♋21ʰ L/W — 1ʰ / Flower from 2ʰ to 20ʰ / Lf 21ʰ

Mercury ☿ ♍ (27 R)	Venus ♀ ♍ 19 ♎	Mars ♂ ♌	Jupiter ♃ ♑ (R)	Saturn ♄ ♑ (R)	Uranus ♅ ♈ (R)	Neptune ♆ ♓ 18 ♒ (R)	Pluto ♇ ♐ (R)

NB: All zodiac symbols refer to astronomical constellations, not astrological signs (see p. 24)

Sep

Planetary aspects
*(**Bold** = visible to naked eye)*

1	
2	♂ ☍ ♆ 18ʰ
3	☾ ☍ ♇ 6ʰ
4	☾ ☌ ♄ 7ʰ
5	☿ △ ♄ 2ʰ ☾ ☍ ♃ 14ʰ
6	♂ △ ♇ 12ʰ ♀ △ ♃ 13ʰ
7	☉ △ ♁ 1ʰ ☽ ☍ ♆ 14ʰ ☽ ☌ ♂ 19ʰ
8	
9	☽ ☌ ☿ 1ʰ
10	☽ ☌ ♀ 5ʰ
11	☽ ☍ ♁ 7ʰ
12	
13	
14	☉ ☍ ♆ 9ʰ
15	
16	☽ ☌ ♇ 6ʰ
17	☉ △ ♇ 2ʰ ☽ ☌ ♄ 4ʰ
18	☽ ☌ ♃ 9ʰ
19	
20	☽ ☌ ♆ 12ʰ ☿ △ ♃ 23ʰ
21	☾ ☍ ♂ 11ʰ
22	
23	☾ ☍ ☿ 2ʰ ♀ ☍ ♁ 10ʰ
24	☾ ☌ ♁ 17ʰ ☾ ☍ ♀ 20ʰ
25	♂ △ ♄ 22ʰ
26	
27	
28	
29	♀ △ ♆ 16ʰ ☉ △ ♄ 22ʰ
30	☾ ☌ ♇ 14ʰ

Planet (naked eye) visibility
Evening: Venus
All night: Jupiter, Saturn
Morning: -

In September there is tension between Earth constellations (with Jupiter and Saturn, and, in the first part of the month, Mercury and Venus), and Warmth constellations with Mars, Uranus and Pluto. There are two Warmth trines and four Earth trines during the month. Only Neptune for the first half of the month is in Watery Pisces.

Northern Transplanting Time
Sep 2 2ʰ to Sep 15 2ʰ and
Sep 29 10ʰ to Oct 12
Southern Transplanting Time
Aug 19 to Sep 1 22ʰ and Sep 15 6ʰ to Sep 29 6ʰ

The times recommended for the **fruit harvest** are those in which the Moon is in Aries or Sagittarius (Sep 14 10ʰ to Sep 16 12ʰ, Sep 23 12ʰ to Sep 25 11ʰ) or other Fruit times.

The harvest of **root crops** is always best undertaken at Root times. Storage trials of onions, carrots, beetroot and potatoes have demonstrated this time and again.

Good times for **sowing winter grain** are when the Moon is in Leo or Sagittarius (Sep 5 3ʰ to Sep 6 8ʰ, and Sep 6 19ʰ to Sep 7 16ʰ, and Sep 14 10ʰ to Sep 16 12ʰ) avoiding unfavourable times, and at other Fruit times.

Rye can if necessary also be sown at Root times with all subsequent cultivations being carried out at Fruit times.

Control slugs by burning between Sep 3 12ʰ and Sep 5 2ʰ or between Sep 30 21ʰ and Oct 2 11ʰ.

Maria Thun's biodynamic tree log preparations
Cut **oak** logs, fill with ground **oak bark** and put them into the ground on Sep 2 between 7ʰ and 24ʰ.

Cut **maple** logs, fill with dried **dandelion** and put them into the ground between Sep 13 22ʰ and Sep 14 15ʰ.

Cut **birch** logs, fill with dried **yarrow** and put them into the ground between Sep 22 23ʰ and Sep 23 16ʰ.

Sep

Unfavourable time

October 2021

All times in GMT

Date	Const. of Moon	Solar & lunar aspects	Trines	Moon El'ment	Parts of the plant enhanced by Moon or planets
1 Fri	♋	☉-♍		W	Leaf
2 Sat	♋♌ 12ʰ			W/H	Leaf to 11ʰ / Fruit from 12ʰ

DST begins in Australia

3 Sun	♌			H	Fruit to 11ʰ / Root from 12ʰ
4 Mon	♌		▲	H	Rt -3ʰ / Fruit from 4ʰ
5 Tue	♌♍ 2ʰ			H/E	1ʰ / Root from 2ʰ
6 Wed	♍	● 11ʰ		E	Root
7 Thu	♍			E	Root
8 Fri	♍♎ 7ʰ	Pg 17:23ʰ		E/L	Root -4ʰ
9 Sat	♎♏ 12ʰ	☊ 20ʰ		L/W	Fl 6ʰ to 11ʰ / Lf 12-15ʰ

10 Sun	♏			W	Leaf from 0ʰ
11 Mon	♏♐ 15ʰ			W/H	Leaf to 14ʰ / Fruit from 15ʰ
12 Tue	♐	☋ 9ʰ		H	Fruit
13 Wed	♐♑ 19ʰ	☽ 3ʰ		H/E	Fruit to 18ʰ / Root 19ʰ
14 Thu	♑			E	Root to 7ʰ
15 Fri	♑♒ 21ʰ	☿ ☍	▲	E/L	Fl 21ʰ
16 Sat	♒			L	Flower

17 Sun	♒♓ 19ʰ			L/W	Flower to 18ʰ / Leaf 19ʰ
18 Mon	♓			W	Leaf
19 Tue	♓			W	Leaf
20 Wed	♓♈ 20ʰ	○ 15ʰ		W/H	Leaf to 19ʰ / Fruit 20ʰ
21 Thu	♈			H	Fruit
22 Fri	♈♉ 20ʰ			H/E	Fruit to 19ʰ / Root 20ʰ
23 Sat	♉	☋ 12ʰ		E	Root to 7ʰ / Root from 16ʰ

24 Sun	♉	Ag 16ʰ		E	Root to 6ʰ / Fruit from 7ʰ to 19ʰ / Root 20ʰ
25 Mon	♉♊ 21ʰ			E/L	Root to 20ʰ / Fl 21ʰ
26 Tue	♊	⌢ 16ʰ		L	Flower
27 Wed	♊			L	Flower
28 Thu	♊♋ 5ʰ	☾ 20ʰ		L/W	Fl to 4ʰ / Leaf from 5ʰ
29 Fri	♋♌ 21ʰ			W/H	Leaf to 20ʰ / Fr 21ʰ
30 Sat	♌			H	Fruit

DST ends in Europe (incl UK and Ireland)

31 Sun	♌			H	Fruit to 21ʰ / 22ʰ

Left margin labels: Northern Tr Time / Southern Transplanting Time / Northern Tr Time

Mercury ☿	Venus ♀	Mars ♂	Jupiter ♃	Saturn ♄	Uranus ⛢	Neptune ♆	Pluto ♇
♍	♎	♌	♑	♑	♈	♒	♐
(R 18 D)	5 ♏		(R 18 D)	(R 11 D)	(R)	(R)	(R 6 D)

NB: All zodiac symbols refer to astronomical constellations, not astrological signs (see p. 24)

Planetary aspects
(**Bold** = *visible to naked eye*)

1 ☾ ☍ ♄ 14ʰ
2 ☾ ☍ ♃ 19ʰ

3
4 ☿ △ ♃ 0ʰ ☾ ☍ ♆ 22ʰ
5
6 ☽ ☌ ♂ 12ʰ ☽ ☌ ☿ 22ʰ
7
8 ☉ ☌ ♂ 4ʰ ☽ ☍ ♅ 13ʰ
9 ☉ ☌ ☿ 16ʰ **☽ ☌ ♀ 20ʰ** ☿ ☌ ♂ 23ʰ

10
11
12
13 ☽ ☌ ♇ 11ʰ
14 **☽ ☌ ♄ 9ʰ**
15 ☿ ☊ 8ʰ ☉ △ ♃ 12ʰ **☽ ☌ ♃ 13ʰ**
16

17 ☽ ☌ ♆ 17ʰ
18
19 ♂ △ ♃ 3ʰ ☽ ☍ ☿ 5ʰ
20 ☽ ☍ ♂ 6ʰ
21 ☾ ☌ ♁ 22ʰ
22
23

24 ☾ ☍ ♀ 22ʰ
25
26
27 ☾ ☍ ♇ 22ʰ
28 ☾ ☍ ♄ 23ʰ
29
30 ☾ ☍ ♃ 4ʰ

31

October continues in the tension between Mercury, Jupiter and Saturn in Earth constellations, reinforced by two Earth trines, and Mars, Uranus and Pluto in Warmth constellations. Neptune is in Light Aquarius and Venus, after Oct 5, is in Watery Scorpio.

Northern Transplanting Time
Sep 29 to Oct 12 7ʰ and
Oct 26 18ʰ to Nov 8
Southern Transplanting Time
Oct 12 11ʰ to Oct 26 14ʰ

Store fruit at any Fruit or Flower time outside Transplanting Time.

Harvest seeds of root plants at Root times, **seeds for leaf plants** at Leaf times, and **seeds for flower plants** at Flower times.

All **cleared ground** should be treated with compost and sprayed with barrel preparation, and ploughed ready for winter.

Control slugs by burning between Sep 30 21ʰ and Oct 2 11ʰ.

Burn feathers or skins of **warm blooded pests** from Oct 22 20ʰ to Oct 25 20ʰ. Ensure the fire is glowing hot (don't use grilling charcoal). Lay dry feathers or skins on the glowing embers. After they have cooled, collect the light grey ash and grind for an hour with a pestle and mortar. This increases their efficacy and the ash can be potentised later. *The burning and grinding should be completed by Oct 25 20ʰ.*

Oct

Planet (naked eye) visibility
Evening: Venus, Saturn
All night: Jupiter
Morning: Mercury (from 16th)

November 2021

Date	Const. of Moon	Solar & lunar aspects	Moon Trines	El'ment
1 Mon	♌︎♍︎13ʰ	☉-♎︎	▲	H/E
2 Tue	♍︎			E
3 Wed	♍︎	☿		E
4 Thu	♍︎♎︎17ʰ	● 21ʰ		E/L
5 Fri	♎︎♏︎22ʰ	**Pg** 22ʰ		L/W
6 Sat	♏︎	☋ 4ʰ		W

DST ends in North America

7 Sun	♏︎♐︎ 23ʰ			W/H
8 Mon	♐︎	☽17ʰ	♀	H
9 Tue	♐︎			H
10 Wed	♑︎ 1ʰ			E
11 Thu	♑︎	☽ 13ʰ		E
12 Fri	♑︎♒︎ 2ʰ		▲	E/L
13 Sat	♒︎			L

14 Sun	♓︎ 0ʰ			W
15 Mon	♓︎			W
16 Tue	♓︎			W
17 Wed	♓︎♈︎ 2ʰ			W/H
18 Thu	♈︎		▲	H
19 Fri	♈︎♉︎ 2ʰ	☉-♏︎, ☉♂︎○ 9ʰ		H/E
20 Sat	♉︎			E

21 Sun	♉︎	**Ag** 2ʰ		E
22 Mon	♉︎♊︎ 3ʰ	⌒ 23ʰ	☿☋	E/L
23 Tue	♊︎			L
24 Wed	♊︎♋︎12ʰ			L/W
25 Thu	♋︎			W
26 Fri	♋︎♌︎ 5ʰ			W/H
27 Sat	♌︎	☾ 12ʰ		H

28 Sun	♌︎♍︎22ʰ			H/E
29 Mon	♍︎		▲	E
30 Tue	♍︎			E

Parts of the plant enhanced by Moon or planets

Vertical labels: Northern Tr Time — Southern Transplanting Time — Northern Tr Time

Chart annotations (0–24 hour scale):
- 1 Mon: Root to 7ʰ / Fr 8ʰ - 12ʰ / Root from 13ʰ
- 2 Tue: Root
- 3 Wed: Root to 16ʰ / 22ʰ
- 4 Thu: Root to 16ʰ / Flower from 17ʰ
- 5 Fri: Flower to 9ʰ
- 6 Sat: Leaf from 11ʰ
- 7 Sun: Leaf to 22ʰ / 23
- 8 Mon: -2ʰ / Fruit from 8ʰ
- 9 Tue: Fruit to 24ʰ
- 10 Wed: Root from 1ʰ
- 11 Thu: Root
- 12 Fri: 1ʰ / Flower from 2ʰ (sp good from 10ʰ to 19ʰ)
- 13 Sat: Flower to 23ʰ
- 14 Sun: Leaf from 0ʰ
- 15 Mon: Leaf
- 16 Tue: Leaf
- 17 Wed: 1ʰ / Fruit from 2ʰ
- 18 Thu: Fruit to 9ʰ / Flower 10ʰ to 19ʰ / Fruit 20ʰ
- 19 Fri: Fruit -4ʰ / 22ʰ ▲ ♌︎18ʰ
- 20 Sat: Root to 16ʰ / Fruit from 17ʰ
- 21 Sun: Fruit to 5ʰ / Root from 6ʰ to 14ʰ
- 22 Mon: Flower from 4ʰ
- 23 Tue: (continued)
- 24 Wed: Flower to 11ʰ / Leaf from 12ʰ
- 25 Thu: Leaf
- 26 Fri: Leaf -4ʰ / Fruit from 5ʰ
- 27 Sat: Fruit
- 28 Sun: Fruit to 21ʰ / 22ʰ
- 29 Mon: 1ʰ / Flower from 2ʰ to 17ʰ / Root 18ʰ
- 30 Tue: Root

0 1 2 3 4 5 6 7 8 9 10 11 12 13 14 15 16 17 18 19 20 21 22 23 24

Mercury ☿	Venus ♀	Mars ♂	Jupiter ♃	Saturn ♄	Uranus ⛢	Neptune ♆	Pluto ♇
♍︎ 11♎︎	♏︎	♌︎	♑︎	♑︎	♈︎	♒︎	♐︎
23♏︎	4 ♐︎	13♎︎			(R)	(R)	

NB: All zodiac symbols refer to astronomical constellations, not astrological signs (see p. 24)

Nov

amic Calendar 2021

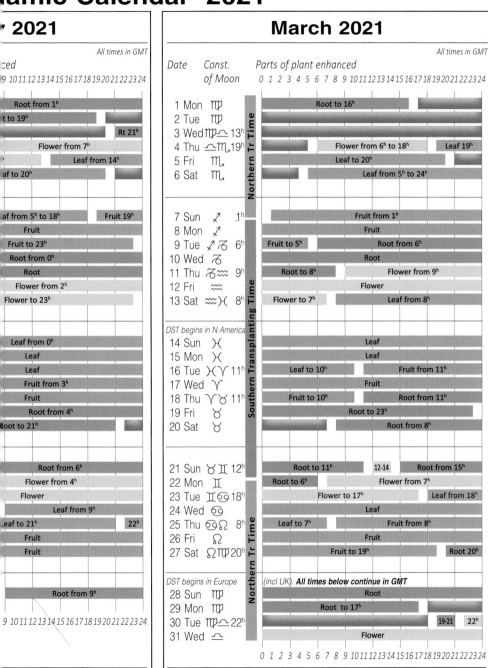

2021

All times in GMT

`ed`

`9 10 11 12 13 14 15 16 17 18 19 20 21 22 23 24`

- Root from 1ʰ
- t to 19ʰ
- Rt 21ʰ
- Flower from 7ʰ
- Leaf from 14ʰ
- af to 20ʰ

- af from 5ʰ to 18ʰ — Fruit 19ʰ
- Fruit
- Fruit to 23ʰ
- Root from 0ʰ
- Root
- Flower from 2ʰ
- Flower to 23ʰ

- Leaf from 0ʰ
- Leaf
- Leaf
- Fruit from 3ʰ
- Fruit
- Root from 4ʰ
- oot to 21ʰ

- Root from 6ʰ
- Flower from 4ʰ
- Flower
- Leaf from 9ʰ
- eaf to 21ʰ — 22ʰ
- Fruit
- Fruit

- Root from 9ʰ

`9 10 11 12 13 14 15 16 17 18 19 20 21 22 23 24`

8 14ʰ and from Feb 23 2ʰ
18ʰ to Feb 22 22ʰ

March 2021

All times in GMT

Date	Const. of Moon	Parts of plant enhanced

`0 1 2 3 4 5 6 7 8 9 10 11 12 13 14 15 16 17 18 19 20 21 22 23 24`

Northern Tr Time

- 1 Mon ♍ — Root to 16ʰ
- 2 Tue ♍
- 3 Wed ♍♎ 13ʰ
- 4 Thu ♎♏ 19ʰ — Flower from 6ʰ to 18ʰ — Leaf 19ʰ
- 5 Fri ♏ — Leaf to 20ʰ
- 6 Sat ♏ — Leaf from 5ʰ to 24ʰ

Southern Transplanting Time

- 7 Sun ♐ 1ʰ — Fruit from 1ʰ
- 8 Mon ♐ — Fruit
- 9 Tue ♐♑ 6ʰ — Fruit to 5ʰ — Root from 6ʰ
- 10 Wed ♑ — Root
- 11 Thu ♑♒ 9ʰ — Root to 8ʰ — Flower from 9ʰ
- 12 Fri ♒ — Flower
- 13 Sat ♒♓ 8ʰ — Flower to 7ʰ — Leaf from 8ʰ

DST begins in N America

- 14 Sun ♓ — Leaf
- 15 Mon ♓ — Leaf
- 16 Tue ♓♈ 11ʰ — Leaf to 10ʰ — Fruit from 11ʰ
- 17 Wed ♈ — Fruit
- 18 Thu ♈♉ 11ʰ — Fruit to 10ʰ — Root from 11ʰ
- 19 Fri ♉ — Root to 23ʰ
- 20 Sat ♉ — Root from 8ʰ

- 21 Sun ♉♊ 12ʰ — Root to 11ʰ — 12-14 — Root from 15ʰ
- 22 Mon ♊ — Root to 6ʰ — Flower from 7ʰ
- 23 Tue ♊♋ 18ʰ — Flower to 17ʰ — Leaf from 18ʰ
- 24 Wed ♋ — Leaf
- 25 Thu ♋♌ 8ʰ — Leaf to 7ʰ — Fruit from 8ʰ
- 26 Fri ♌ — Fruit
- 27 Sat ♌♍ 20ʰ — Fruit to 19ʰ — Root 20ʰ

DST begins in Europe (incl UK). **All times below continue in GMT**

Northern Tr Time

- 28 Sun ♍ — Root
- 29 Mon ♍ — Root to 17ʰ
- 30 Tue ♍♎ 22ʰ — 19-21 — 22ʰ
- 31 Wed ♎ — Flower

`0 1 2 3 4 5 6 7 8 9 10 11 12 13 14 15 16 17 18 19 20 21 22 23 24`

Northern Transplanting Time to March 7 19ʰ and from March 22 11ʰ
Southern Transplanting Time March 7 23ʰ to March 22 7ʰ

July 2021

All times in GMT

Date	Const. of Moon	Parts of plant enhanced
1 Thu	♓	Leaf
2 Fri	♓	Leaf
3 Sat	♓♈ 12ʰ	Leaf to 11ʰ / Fruit from 12ʰ
4 Sun	♈	Fruit
5 Mon	♈♉ 13ʰ	Fruit to 12ʰ / Fl 13ʰ to 18ʰ / Root 19ʰ
6 Tue	♉	Root to 18ʰ
7 Wed	♉	Root from 3ʰ
8 Thu	♉♊ 14ʰ	Root to 13ʰ / Flower from 14ʰ
9 Fri	♊	Flower
10 Sat	♊♋ 20ʰ	Flower to 19ʰ / Leaf 20ʰ
11 Sun	♋	Leaf
12 Mon	♋♌ 12ʰ	Leaf to 7ʰ / Flower from 8ʰ
13 Tue	♌	-2ʰ / Fruit from 3ʰ
14 Wed	♌	Fruit
15 Thu	♌♍ 4ʰ	Fr -3ʰ / Root from 4ʰ
16 Fri	♍	Root
17 Sat	♍	Root
18 Sun	♍♎ 12ʰ	Root to 8ʰ
19 Mon	♎♏ 18ʰ	22ʰ
20 Tue	♏	Leaf to 8ʰ / Lf 17ʰ-21ʰ
21 Wed	♏♐ 21ʰ	23
22 Thu	♐	Fruit
23 Fri	♐♑ 22ʰ	Fruit to 21ʰ / 22ʰ
24 Sat	♑	Root
25 Sun	♑♒ 22ʰ	Root to 21ʰ / 22ʰ
26 Mon	♒	Flower
27 Tue	♒♓ 19ʰ	Flower to 18ʰ / Leaf 19ʰ
28 Wed	♓	Leaf
29 Thu	♓	Leaf
30 Fri	♓♈ 20ʰ	Leaf to 19ʰ / Fruit 20ʰ
31 Sat	♈	Fruit

Southern Tr Time (3 Sat – 10 Sat)
Northern Transplanting Time (11 Sun – 24 Sat)
Southern Transplanting Time (25 Sun – 31 Sat)

In UK/Ireland remember to add 1 hour for Daylight Saving Time

Northern Transplanting Time July 9 12ʰ to July 22 13ʰ
Southern Transplanting Time June 25 to July 9 8ʰ & from July 22 17ʰ

Augu...

Date	Const. of Moon	Parts of plant e...
1 Sun	♈♉ 20ʰ	
2 Mon	♉	Flower t...
3 Tue	♉	
4 Wed	♉♊ 21ʰ	
5 Thu	♊	
6 Fri	♊	
7 Sat	♊♋ 4ʰ	Fl -3ʰ
8 Sun	♋♌ 19ʰ	
9 Mon	♌	
10 Tue	♌	
11 Wed	♌♍ 9ʰ	Fruit to 8ʰ
12 Thu	♍	
13 Fri	♍	
14 Sat	♍♎ 17ʰ	R...
15 Sun	♎	
16 Mon	♏ 0ʰ	Leaf from 0...
17 Tue	♏	
18 Wed	♏♐ 4ʰ	Lf -3ʰ
19 Thu	♐	
20 Fri	♐♑ 7ʰ	Fruit to 11ʰ (sp...
21 Sat	♑	
22 Sun	♑♒ 7ʰ	Fruit to...
23 Mon	♒	Flower to 6ʰ
24 Tue	♒♓ 4ʰ	Fl -3ʰ
25 Wed	♓	Le...
26 Thu	♓	
27 Fri	♓♈ 4ʰ	
28 Sat	♈	
29 Sun	♈♉ 4ʰ	
30 Mon	♉	
31 Tue	♉	

S T T
Northern Transplanting Time
Southern Transplanting Time

Northern Transplanting Time Au...
Southern Transplanting Time to...

October 2021

Date	Const. of Moon	Parts of plant enhanced (0–24)
1 Fri	♋	Leaf
2 Sat	♋♌ 12ʰ	Leaf to 11ʰ / Fruit from 12ʰ
DST begins in Australia		
3 Sun	♌	Fruit to 11ʰ / Root from 12ʰ
4 Mon	♌	Rt -3ʰ / Fruit from 4ʰ
5 Tue	♌♍ 2ʰ	1ʰ / Root from 2ʰ
6 Wed	♍	Root
7 Thu	♍	Root
8 Fri	♍♎ 7ʰ	Root -4ʰ
9 Sat	♎♏ 12ʰ	Fl 6ʰ to 11ʰ / Lf 12-15ʰ
10 Sun	♏	Leaf from 0ʰ
11 Mon	♏♐ 15ʰ	Leaf to 14ʰ / Fruit from 15ʰ
12 Tue	♐	Fruit
13 Wed	♐♑ 19ʰ	Fruit to 18ʰ / Root 19ʰ
14 Thu	♑	Root to 7ʰ
15 Fri	♑♒ 21ʰ	Fl 21ʰ
16 Sat	♒	Flower
17 Sun	♒♓ 19ʰ	Flower to 18ʰ / Leaf 19ʰ
18 Mon	♓	Leaf
19 Tue	♓	Leaf
20 Wed	♓♈ 20ʰ	Leaf to 19ʰ / Fruit 20ʰ
21 Thu	♈	Fruit
22 Fri	♈♉ 20ʰ	Fruit to 19ʰ / Root 20ʰ
23 Sat	♉	Root to 7ʰ / Root from 16ʰ
24 Sun	♉	Root to 6ʰ / Fruit from 7ʰ to 19ʰ / Root 20ʰ
25 Mon	♉♊ 21ʰ	Root to 20ʰ / Fl 21ʰ
26 Tue	♊	Flower
27 Wed	♊	Flower
28 Thu	♊♋ 5ʰ	Fl to 4ʰ / Leaf from 5ʰ
29 Fri	♋♌ 21ʰ	Leaf to 20ʰ / Fr 21ʰ
30 Sat	♌	Fruit
DST ends in Europe (incl UK and Ireland)		
31 Sun	♌	Fruit to 21ʰ / 22ʰ

Northern Tr Time — applies 1–8 Fri; *Southern Transplanting Time* — 9–30; *Northern Tr Time* — 24–31

Northern Transplanting Time to Oct 12 7ʰ and from Oct 26 18ʰ
Southern Transplanting Time Oct 12 11ʰ to Oct 26 14ʰ

Novem...

Date	Const. of Moon	Parts of plant e... (0–6)
1 Mon	♌♍ 13ʰ	Root to 7ʰ
2 Tue	♍	
3 Wed	♍	R...
4 Thu	♍♎ 17ʰ	F...
5 Fri	♎♏ 22ʰ	Flower to 9...
6 Sat	♏	
DST ends in N America		
7 Sun	♏♐ 23ʰ	
8 Mon	♐	-2ʰ
9 Tue	♐	
10 Wed	♑ 1ʰ	
11 Thu	♑	
12 Fri	♑♒ 2ʰ	1ʰ / Flo...
13 Sat	♒	
14 Sun	♓ 0ʰ	
15 Mon	♓	
16 Tue	♓	
17 Wed	♓♈ 2ʰ	1ʰ
18 Thu	♈	Fruit to 9...
19 Fri	♈♉ 2ʰ	Fruit -4ʰ
20 Sat	♉	R...
21 Sun	♉	Fruit to 5ʰ
22 Mon	♉♊ 3ʰ	
23 Tue	♊	
24 Wed	♊♋ 12ʰ	Flower t...
25 Thu	♋	
26 Fri	♋♌ 5ʰ	Leaf -4ʰ
27 Sat	♌	
28 Sun	♌♍ 22ʰ	1ʰ / Fl...
29 Mon	♍	
30 Tue	♍	

0 1 2 3 4 5 6

Northern Transplanting Time to...
Southern Transplanting Time N...

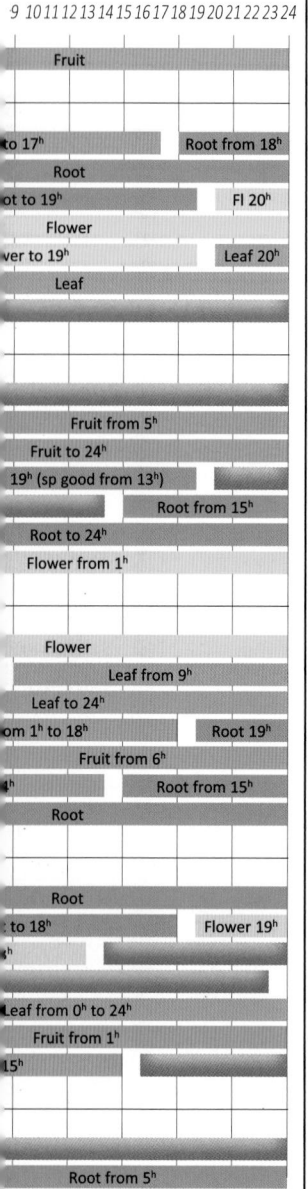

ced

9 10 11 12 13 14 15 16 17 18 19 20 21 22 23 24

Fruit	
to 17ʰ	Root from 18ʰ
Root	
ot to 19ʰ	Fl 20ʰ
Flower	
ver to 19ʰ	Leaf 20ʰ
Leaf	
Fruit from 5ʰ	
Fruit to 24ʰ	
19ʰ (sp good from 13ʰ)	
	Root from 15ʰ
Root to 24ʰ	
Flower from 1ʰ	
Flower	
Leaf from 9ʰ	
Leaf to 24ʰ	
om 1ʰ to 18ʰ	Root 19ʰ
Fruit from 6ʰ	
4ʰ	Root from 15ʰ
Root	
Root	
to 18ʰ	Flower 19ʰ
ʰ	
Leaf from 0ʰ to 24ʰ	
Fruit from 1ʰ	
15ʰ	
Root from 5ʰ	

1 8ʰ and May 16 0ʰ to May 28 17ʰ
to May 15 20ʰ & from May 28 21ʰ

June 2021

All times in GMT

In UK/Ireland remember to add 1 hour for Daylight Saving Time

Date	Const. of Moon	Parts of plant enhanced (0–24)
1 Tue	♑♒ 4ʰ	Rt -3ʰ · Flower from 4ʰ
2 Wed	♒	Flower
3 Thu	♒♓ 2ʰ	1ʰ · Leaf from 2ʰ to 12ʰ · Root 13ʰ to 20ʰ · Fl 21ʰ
4 Fri	♓	Fl -3ʰ · Leaf from 4ʰ
5 Sat	♓	Leaf
6 Sun	♓♈ 6ʰ	Leaf to 5ʰ · Fruit from 6ʰ
7 Mon	♈	Fruit
8 Tue	♈♉ 6ʰ	Fruit to 5ʰ · Root from 6ʰ
9 Wed	♉	Root to 12ʰ · Rt 21ʰ
10 Thu	♉	Root to 8ʰ · Root from 14ʰ
11 Fri	♉♊ 7ʰ	Root to 6ʰ · Flower from 7ʰ
12 Sat	♊	Flower
13 Sun	♊♋ 14ʰ	Flower to 13ʰ · Leaf from 14ʰ
14 Mon	♋	Leaf
15 Tue	♋♌ 6ʰ	Leaf to 5ʰ · Fruit from 6ʰ
16 Wed	♌	Fruit
17 Thu	♌♍ 22ʰ	Fruit to 21ʰ · 22ʰ
18 Fri	♍	Root
19 Sat	♍	Root
20 Sun	♍	Root
21 Mon	♍♎ 4ʰ	Rt -3ʰ · Flower from 4ʰ
22 Tue	♎♏ 10ʰ	Flower to 9ʰ · Leaf from 10ʰ to 21ʰ
23 Wed	♏	23
24 Thu	♏♐ 11ʰ	Leaf to 10ʰ · Fruit from 11ʰ
25 Fri	♐	Fruit
26 Sat	♐♑ 12ʰ	Fruit to 11ʰ · Root from 12ʰ
27 Sun	♑	Root
28 Mon	♑♒ 12ʰ	Root to 11ʰ · Flower from 12ʰ
29 Tue	♒	Flower
30 Wed	♒♓ 10ʰ	Flower to 9ʰ · Leaf from 10ʰ

0 1 2 3 4 5 6 7 8 9 10 11 12 13 14 15 16 17 18 19 20 21 22 23 24

Southern Transplanting Time — *Northern Transplanting Time* — *Southern Tr Time*

Northern Transplanting Time June 12 6ʰ to June 25 4ʰ
Southern Transplanting Time to June 12 2ʰ and June 25 8ʰ to July 9

The Maria Thun Biody[...]

January 2021

All times in GMT

Date	Const. of Moon	Parts of plant enhanced
1 Fri	♋	Leaf
2 Sat	♋♌ 6ʰ	Leaf to 5ʰ — Fruit from 6ʰ
3 Sun	♌	Fruit
4 Mon	♌♍ 19ʰ	Fruit to 18ʰ — Root 19ʰ
5 Tue	♍	Root
6 Wed	♍	Root
7 Thu	♍	Root
8 Fri	♍♎ 2ʰ	1ʰ — Flower from 2ʰ
9 Sat	♎♏ 8ʰ	Fl -3ʰ
10 Sun	♏	Leaf from 5ʰ to 15ʰ
11 Mon	♏♐ 12ʰ	Leaf from 0ʰ to 11ʰ — Fruit from 12ʰ
12 Tue	♐	Fruit
13 Wed	♐♑ 15ʰ	Fruit to 14ʰ — 15-17 — Fruit from 18ʰ
14 Thu	♑	Fr -3ʰ — Root from 4ʰ
15 Fri	♑♒ 17ʰ	Rt -3ʰ
16 Sat	♒	
17 Sun	♒♓ 16ʰ	Flower from 1ʰ to 15ʰ — Leaf from 16ʰ
18 Mon	♓	Leaf
19 Tue	♓	Leaf
20 Wed	♓♈ 19ʰ	Leaf to 18ʰ — Fruit 19ʰ
21 Thu	♈	Fruit
22 Fri	♈♉ 19ʰ	Fruit to 18ʰ — Root 19ʰ
23 Sat	♉	Root to 9ʰ
24 Sun	♉	
25 Mon	♉♊ 19ʰ	Root from 2ʰ to 18ʰ — Flower 19ʰ
26 Tue	♊	Flower
27 Wed	♊♋ 23ʰ	Flower to 22ʰ — 23
28 Thu	♋	Leaf
29 Fri	♋♌ 13ʰ	Leaf to 12ʰ — Fruit from 13ʰ
30 Sat	♌	Fruit
31 Sun	♌	Fruit to 24ʰ

Northern Tr Time (Jan 1–2)
Southern Transplanting Time (Jan 12–26)
Northern Tr Time (Jan 26–31)

Northern Transplanting Time Dec 30 to Jan 12 6ʰ and from Jan 26 17ʰ
Southern Transplanting Time Jan 12 10ʰ to Jan 26 13ʰ

Februa[ry]

Date	Const. of Moon	Parts of plant e[nhanced]
1 Mon	♍ 1ʰ	
2 Tue	♍	
3 Wed	♍	
4 Thu	♍♎ 7ʰ	Root to 6ʰ
5 Fri	♎♏ 14ʰ	Flower
6 Sat	♏	
7 Sun	♏♐ 19ʰ	
8 Mon	♐	
9 Tue	♐	
10 Wed	♑ 0ʰ	
11 Thu	♑	
12 Fri	♑♒ 2ʰ	1ʰ
13 Sat	♒	
14 Sun	♓ 0ʰ	
15 Mon	♓	
16 Tue	♓	
17 Wed	♓♈ 3ʰ	-2ʰ
18 Thu	♈	
19 Fri	♈♉ 4ʰ	Fr -3ʰ
20 Sat	♉	
21 Sun	♉	Rt -3ʰ
22 Mon	♉♊ 4ʰ	
23 Tue	♊	
24 Wed	♊♋ 9ʰ	Flower to 8ʰ
25 Thu	♋♌ 22ʰ	
26 Fri	♌	
27 Sat	♌	
28 Sun	♌♍ 9ʰ	Fruit to 8ʰ

0 1 2 3 4 5 6

Northern Transplanting Time to F[...]
Southern Transplanting Time Fe[...]

namic Calendar 2021

t 2021

All times in GMT

nced

3 9 10 11 12 13 14 15 16 17 18 19 20 21 22 23 24

uit to 19ʰ | 20-22 | 23
Root from 12ʰ to 22ʰ
7-10ʰ | Root from 11ʰ
Root to 20ʰ | Fl 21ʰ
Flower
Flower
Leaf from 4ʰ

af to 18ʰ | Fruit 19ʰ
Fruit
Fruit
Root from 9ʰ
Root
Root
o 16ʰ | Flower from 17ʰ

Flower to 23ʰ
1ʰ
| 22ʰ
Fruit from 4ʰ
Fruit

2ʰ-6ʰ) | Root from 12ʰ
t to 18ʰ | Fruit 19ʰ

Flower from 12ʰ
Root from 7ʰ to 16ʰ | Flower from 17ʰ
Leaf from 4ʰ
15ʰ

Fruit from 5ʰ to 20ʰ

Flower 18ʰ-24ʰ
Root from 9ʰ
Root

8 9 10 11 12 13 14 15 16 17 18 19 20 21 22 23 24

19ʰ to Aug 18 20ʰ
g 5 15ʰ and from Aug 19 0ʰ

September 2021

All times in GMT

Date	Const. of Moon	Parts of plant enhanced (0 1 2 3 4 5 6 7 8 9 10 11 12 13 14 15 16 17 18 19 20 21 22 23 24)
1 Wed ♉Ⅱ 5ʰ		Root to 4ʰ — Flower from 5ʰ
2 Thu Ⅱ		Flower
3 Fri Ⅱ♋ 12ʰ		Flower to 11ʰ — Leaf from 12ʰ
4 Sat ♋		Leaf to 19ʰ — Root 20ʰ
5 Sun ♋♌ 3ʰ		Root to 5ʰ — Fruit from 6ʰ
6 Mon ♌		Fr to 8ʰ (sp good) — Root 9ʰ to 16ʰ — Fruit 17ʰ (sp gd)
7 Tue ♌♍ 17ʰ		Fruit to 16ʰ (sp good to 4ʰ) — Root from 17ʰ
8 Wed ♍		Root
9 Thu ♍		Root
10 Fri ♍♎ 23ʰ		Root to 21ʰ
11 Sat ♎		23
12 Sun ♎♏ 5ʰ		Fl to 4ʰ — Leaf 5ʰ to 12ʰ — Lf 21ʰ
13 Mon ♏		Leaf
14 Tue ♏♐ 10ʰ		Leaf to 9ʰ — Fruit from 10ʰ
15 Wed ♐		Fruit
16 Thu ♐♑ 13ʰ		Fruit to 12ʰ — Root from 13ʰ
17 Fri ♑		Root
18 Sat ♑♒ 15ʰ		Root to 14ʰ — Flower from 15ʰ
19 Sun ♒		Flower
20 Mon ♒♓ 12ʰ		Flower to 11ʰ — Lf 12-16ʰ — Root from 17ʰ
21 Tue ♓		-2ʰ — Leaf from 3ʰ
22 Wed ♓		Leaf
23 Thu ♓♈ 12ʰ		Leaf to 11ʰ — Fruit from 12ʰ
24 Fri ♈		Fruit
25 Sat ♈♉ 12ʰ		Fruit to 11ʰ — Root from 12ʰ
DST begins in NZ		
26 Sun ♉		Rt -3ʰ — Fruit from 13ʰ
27 Mon ♉		1ʰ — Root from 2ʰ
28 Tue ♉Ⅱ 13ʰ		Root to 12ʰ — Flower from 13ʰ
29 Wed Ⅱ		Flower to 17ʰ (sp good from 9ʰ) — Root from 18ʰ
30 Thu Ⅱ♋ 21ʰ		1ʰ — Flower from 2ʰ to 20ʰ — Lf 21ʰ

0 1 2 3 4 5 6 7 8 9 10 11 12 13 14 15 16 17 18 19 20 21 22 23 24

Northern Transplanting Time (vertical label)
Southern Transplanting Time (vertical label)

In UK/Ireland remember to add 1 hour for Daylight Saving Time (vertical label)

Northern Transplanting Time Sep 2 2ʰ to Sep 15 2ʰ & from Sep 29 10ʰ
Southern Transplanting Time to Sep 1 22ʰ and Sep 15 6ʰ to Sep 29 6ʰ

nced

9 10 11 12 13 14 15 16 17 18 19 20 21 22 23 24

Fr 8ʰ - 12ʰ	Root from 13ʰ
Root	
ʇo 16ʰ	22ʰ
ʇo 16ʰ	Flower from 17ʰ
	Leaf from 11ʰ
Leaf to 22ʰ	23
	Fruit from 8ʰ
Fruit to 24ʰ	
Root from 1ʰ	
Root	
from 2ʰ (sp good from 10ʰ to 19ʰ)	
Flower to 23ʰ	
Leaf from 0ʰ	
Leaf	
Leaf	
Fruit from 2ʰ	
Flower 10ʰ to 19ʰ	Fruit 20ʰ
	22ʰ
ʇo 16ʰ	Fruit from 17ʰ
from 6ʰ to 14ʰ	
Flower from 4ʰ	
	Leaf from 12ʰ
Leaf	
Fruit from 5ʰ	
Fruit	
Fruit to 21ʰ	22ʰ
from 2ʰ to 17ʰ	Root 18ʰ
Root	

8 9 10 11 12 13 14 15 16 17 18 19 20 21 22 23 24

ʋv 8 15ʰ and from Nov 23 1ʰ

8 19ʰ to Nov 22 21ʰ

December 2021

Date	Const. of Moon		Parts of plant enhanced

0 1 2 3 4 5 6 7 8 9 10 11 12 13 14 15 16 17 18 19 20 21 22 23 24

Northern Tr Time

1 Wed	♍		Root
2 Thu	♍♎ 4ʰ		Rt -3ʰ / Flower from 4ʰ to 22ʰ
3 Fri	♎♏ 9ʰ		Fl 4ʰ-8ʰ / 19-21
4 Sat	♏		23

Southern Transplanting Time

5 Sun	♏♐ 10ʰ		Leaf to 9ʰ / Fruit from 10ʰ
6 Mon	♐		Fruit
7 Tue	♐♑ 10ʰ		Fruit to 9ʰ / Root from 10ʰ
8 Wed	♑		Root
9 Thu	♑♒ 9ʰ		Root to 8ʰ / Flower from 9ʰ
10 Fri	♒		Flower
11 Sat	♒♓ 6ʰ		Flower to 5ʰ / Leaf from 6ʰ
12 Sun	♓		Leaf
13 Mon	♓		Leaf
14 Tue	♓♈ 8ʰ		Leaf to 7ʰ / Fruit from 8ʰ
15 Wed	♈		Fruit
16 Thu	♈♉ 8ʰ		Fruit to 7ʰ / Root from 8ʰ to 19ʰ
17 Fri	♉		Root from 4ʰ to 16ʰ / Flower from 17ʰ
18 Sat	♉		Fl to 4ʰ

Northern Transplanting Time

19 Sun	♉♊ 9ʰ		
20 Mon	♊		21-23
21 Tue	♊♋ 18ʰ		Flower from 0ʰ to 17ʰ / Leaf from 18ʰ
22 Wed	♋		Leaf
23 Thu	♋♌ 11ʰ		Leaf to 10ʰ / Fruit from 11ʰ
24 Fri	♌		Fruit
25 Sat	♌		Fruit
26 Sun	♌♍ 5ʰ		Fruit -4ʰ / Root from 5ʰ
27 Mon	♍		Root
28 Tue	♍		Root
29 Wed	♍♎ 14ʰ		Root to 13ʰ / Flower from 14ʰ
30 Thu	♎♏ 20ʰ		Flower to 19ʰ
31 Fri	♏		Leaf from 5ʰ

0 1 2 3 4 5 6 7 8 9 10 11 12 13 14 15 16 17 18 19 20 21 22 23 24

Northern T'planting Time to Dec 6 1ʰ and from Dec 20 7ʰ to Jan 2
Southern Transplanting Time Dec 6 5ʰ to Dec 20 3ʰ

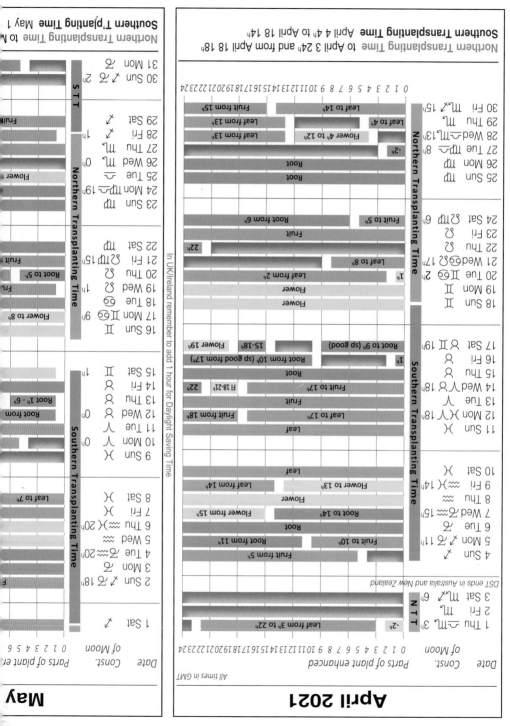

Planetary aspects
*(**Bold** = visible to naked eye)*

1	☿△♃ 4ʰ ☾☌♆ 7ʰ
2	
3	**☾•☿ 19ʰ**
4	**☾☌♂ 6ʰ** ☽☍♀ 21ʰ
5	☉☍♀ 0ʰ
6	
7	
8	☽•♀ 5ʰ
9	☽☌♇ 18ʰ
10	☿☌♂ 13ʰ ☽☌♄ 16ʰ
11	☽☌♃ 20ʰ
12	☉△♆ 16ʰ
13	☿☍♀ 16ʰ ☽☌♆ 22ʰ
14	
15	
16	
17	♂☍♀ 17ʰ
18	☽☌♀ 3ʰ ☽☍♂ 3ʰ ☿△♆ 16ʰ ☽☍☿ 20ʰ
19	♀△♀ 6ʰ
20	
21	
22	☿☋ 15ʰ
23	☾☍♀ 11ʰ
24	☾☍♇ 6ʰ
25	☾☍♄ 9ʰ
26	☾☍♃ 16ʰ
27	
28	☾☍♆ 16ʰ
29	☉☌☿ 5ʰ ♂△♆ 14ʰ
30	

Planet (naked eye) visibility
Evening: Venus, Jupiter, Saturn
All night: -
Morning: Mercury (to 12th), Mars (from 26th)

Jupiter and Saturn (as well as Mercury until Nov 11) are in Earth constellations, balanced by Uranus, Pluto and Venus (after Nov 4) in Warmth constellations. There are two Light trines and for a time Mercury and Mars are in Light constellations, which may ensure some brightness.

Northern Transplanting Time
Oct 26 to Nov 8 15ʰ and
Nov 23 1ʰ to Dec 6
Southern Transplanting Time
Nov 8 19ʰ to Nov 22 21ʰ

The Flower times in Transplanting Time are ideal for **planting flower bulbs,** showing vigorous growth and vivid colours. The remaining Flower times should only be considered as back up, as bulbs planted on those times will not flower so freely.

If not already completed in October, all organic waste materials should be gathered and made into a **compost.** Applying the biodynamic preparations to the compost will ensure a rapid transformation and good fungal development. An application of barrel preparation will also help the composting process.

Fruit and forest trees will also benefit at this time from a spraying of horn manure and/or barrel preparation when being transplanted.

Best times for **cutting Advent greenery** and **Christmas trees** for transporting are Flower times, avoiding unfavourable times.

Burn **fly papers** in the cow barn at Flower times.

Maria Thun's tree log preparations (SH only)
Cut **maple** logs, fill with **dandelion** and put them into the ground between Nov 4 13ʰ and Nov 5 6ʰ.

Cut **larch** logs, fill with dried **camomile** and put them into the ground on Nov 13 between 5ʰ and 22ʰ.

Cut **oak** logs, fill with ground **oak bark** and put them into the ground between Nov 17 6ʰ and Nov 18 1ʰ.

Unfavourable time

December 2021

All times in GMT

Date	Const. of Moon	Solar & lunar aspects	Moon Trines	El'ment	Parts of the plant enhanced by Moon or planets

Date	Const. of Moon	Solar & lunar aspects	Moon Trines	El'ment	
1 Wed	♍	☉-♏		E	Root
2 Thu	♍♎ 4ʰ			E/L	Rt -3ʰ / Flower from 4ʰ to 22ʰ
3 Fri	♎♏ 9ʰ	☋ 15ʰ	☌♂	L/W	Fl 4ʰ-8ʰ / 19-21
4 Sat	♏	☉☌● 8ʰ Pg 10ʰ		W	23 ☌☿
5 Sun	♏♐ 10ʰ			W/H	Leaf to 9ʰ / Fruit from 10ʰ
6 Mon	♐	☽ 3ʰ		H	Fruit
7 Tue	♐♑ 10ʰ			H/E	Fruit to 9ʰ / Root from 10ʰ
8 Wed	♑			E	Root
9 Thu	♑♒ 9ʰ			E/L	Root to 8ʰ / Flower from 9ʰ
10 Fri	♒			L	Flower
11 Sat	♒♓ 6ʰ	☽ 2ʰ		L/W	Flower to 5ʰ / Leaf from 6ʰ
12 Sun	♓			W	Leaf
13 Mon	♓			W	Leaf
14 Tue	♓♈ 8ʰ			W/H	Leaf to 7ʰ / Fruit from 8ʰ
15 Wed	♈			H	Fruit
16 Thu	♈♉ 8ʰ			H/E	Fruit to 7ʰ / Root from 8ʰ to 19ʰ
17 Fri	♉	♌ 0ʰ		E	Root from 4ʰ to 16ʰ / Flower from 17ʰ
18 Sat	♉	Ag 2ʰ		E	Fl to 4ʰ
19 Sun	♉♊ 9ʰ	○ 5ʰ	♂☋	E/L	21-23
20 Mon	♊	☉-♐ ⌒ 5ʰ	▲	L	♀☋
21 Tue	♊♋ 18ʰ			L/W	Flower from 0ʰ to 17ʰ / Leaf from 18ʰ
22 Wed	♋			W	Leaf
23 Thu	♋♌ 11ʰ			W/H	Leaf to 10ʰ / Fruit from 11ʰ
24 Fri	♌			H	Fruit
25 Sat	♌	Christmas		H	Fruit
26 Sun	♌♍ 5ʰ			H/E	Fruit -4ʰ / Root from 5ʰ
27 Mon	♍	☽ 2ʰ		E	Root
28 Tue	♍			E	Root
29 Wed	♍♎ 14ʰ			E/L	Root to 13ʰ / Flower from 14ʰ
30 Thu	♎♏ 20ʰ			L/W	Flower to 19ʰ
31 Fri	♏	☋ 1ʰ		W	Leaf from 5ʰ

Northern Tr Time / Southern Transplanting Time / Northern Transplanting Time

Mercury ☿	Venus ♀	Mars ♂	Jupiter ♃	Saturn ♄	Uranus ♅	Neptune ♆	Pluto ♇
♏	♐	♎	♑	♑	♈	♒	♐
12 ♐	(19 R)	10 ♏	9 ♒		(R)	(R 1 D)	

NB: All zodiac symbols refer to astronomical constellations, not astrological signs (see p. 24)

Dec

Planetary aspects
(**Bold** = *visible to naked eye*)

December 2021

1	
2	☾ ☍ ⯝ 7h
3	**☾ ☌ ♂ 1h**
4	☾ ● ☿ 13h
5	
6	
7	☾ ☌ ♀ 1h ☾ ☌ ♇ 4h
8	☾ ☌ ♄ 4h
9	☾ ☌ ♃ 9h
10	
11	☾ ☌ ♆ 4h ♀ ☌ ♇ 16h
12	
13	
14	
15	☾ ☌ ⯝ 7h
16	
17	☾ ☍ ♂ 2h
18	
19	♂ ⯒ 17h
20	**☾ ☍ ☿ 6h** ♀ ⯒ 8h ☿ △ ⯝ 20h
21	**☾ ☍ ♇ 13h** **☾ ☍ ♀ 15h**
22	**☾ ☌ ♄ 19h**
23	
24	**☾ ☍ ♃ 7h**
25	♀ ☌ ♇ 12h **☾ ☍ ♆ 23h**
26	
27	
28	
29	☿ ☌ ♀ 10h **☾ ☍ ⯝ 16h**
30	☿ ☌ ♇ 10h
31	**☾ ☌ ♂ 20h**

December has a mixed picture: Jupiter and Saturn remain in the cold Earth constellation of Capricorn, but Pluto and Uranus together with Venus in the first half, and Mercury in the second half of the month are in Warmth constellations. Until Dec 10 Mars is in a Light constellation, as is Neptune for the whole month. Mercury begins in Watery Scorpio, and leaves just after Mars reaches Scorpio.

Northern Transplanting Time
Nov 23 to Dec 6 1h and
Dec 20 7h to Jan 2
Southern Transplanting Time
Dec 6 5h to Dec 20 3h

The transplanting time is good for **pruning trees and hedges.** Fruit trees should be pruned at Fruit or Flower times.

Best times for cutting **Advent greenery** and **Christmas trees** are at Flower times to ensure lasting fragrance.

Southern hemisphere:
Harvest time for seeds (always avoiding unfavourable times):
Leaf seeds: Leaf times.
Fruit seeds: Fruit times, preferably with Moon in Leo (Dec 23 11h to Dec 26 4h).
Root seeds: Dec 26 5h to Dec 29 13h, and at other Root times.
Flower seeds: Dec 9 9h to Dec 11 5h, and at other Flower times.

Control slugs: Dec 21 18h to Dec 23 10h.

We wish all our readers a blessed festive time and the best of health for the New Year of 2022

Planet (naked eye) visibility
Evening: Venus, Jupiter, Saturn
All night:
Morning: Mars

Sowing times for trees and shrubs

Sowing times depend on planetary aspects and are not specific to either northern or southern hemispheres. For trees and shrubs not mentioned here, sow at an appropriate time of the Moon's position in the zodiac, depending on the part of the tree or shrub to be enhanced. Avoid unfavourable times.

Sowing times are different from transplanting times. Seedlings should be transplanted during the descending Moon when the Moon is in a constellation corresponding to the part of the tree to to be enhanced. It is important to remember that seedlings need to sufficiently mature to withstand the winter. The time of sowing should therefore chime with local conditions and take account of the germination habit of each tree species.

Note that some species (marked in **bold**) appear in two groups.

*Alder, **Apricot**, Elm, **Larch**, Peach:*
  July 25 9^h to July 26 2^h;
  Aug 1 11^h to Aug 2 4^h;
  Aug 10 14^h to Aug 11 7^h;
  Aug 24 14^h to Aug 25 7^h *(also Magnolia)*;
  Nov 13 5^h to 22^h.

*Apple, **Apricot**, Copper beech, Damson, Maple, Olive, **Peach**, **Sweet chestnut**, Walnut:*
  July 22 2^h to 19^h;
  July 29 5^h to 22^h;
  Aug 10 14^h to Aug 11 7^h;
  Aug 19 13^h to Aug 20 6^h.

*Ash, **Cedar**, **Fir**, Hazel, **Mirabelle plum**, Rowan, **Spruce** (* = also Hawthorn):*
  July 17 12^h to July 18 5^h;
  * Aug 1 19^h to Aug 2 12^h;
  Aug 19 13^h to Aug 20 6^h;
  Sep 13 22^h to Sep 14 15^h;
  * Nov 4 13^h to Nov 5 6^h.

*Beech, **Cedar**, **Fir**, Hornbeam, Juniper, Palm, Pine, Plum, Quince, Sloe, **Spruce**, Thuja:*
  July 1 2^h to 19^h;
  July 6 16^h to July 7 9^h;
  Aug 1 11^h to Aug 2 12^h.

*Birch, **Larch**, Lime tree, **Mirabelle plum**, Pear, Robinia, Willow:*
  (June 23 23^h to June 24 6^h);
  July 6 16^h to July 7 9^h;
  July 22 2^h to 19^h;
  Aug 9 13^h to Aug 10 6^h *(also Magnolia)*;
  Sep 22 23^h to Sep 23 16^h.

Blackcurrant:
  Sep 22 23^h to Sep 23 16^h;
  Nov 4 13^h to Nov 5 6^h;
  Nov 13 5^h to 22^h;
  Nov 17 6^h to 23^h.

*Cherry, Chestnut, Horse chestnut (Buckeye), Oak, **Sweet chestnut**, Yew (* = also Mulberry):*
  * June 5 9^h to June 6 2^h;
  July 1 2^h to 19^h;
  July 29 5^h to 22^h *(also Rose hip)*;
  * Sep 2 7^h to 24^h;
  * Nov 17 6^h to 23^h.

Lilac, Poplar, Sallow, Snowberry:
  Sep 22 23^h to Sep 23 16^h;
  Nov 13 5^h to 22^h.

Felling times for trees

The times given are to ensure the best quality and durability of the timber.

If a large number of these trees need to be felled in the short time available, cut the bark all around the trunk to stop sap flow. The actual felling can be done later.

Those trees which are not listed should be felled at the end of the growing season at Flower times. Avoid unfavourable times.

*Alder, **Apricot,** Elm, **Larch,** Peach:*
  May 2 3^h to 12^h;
  May 12 13^h to 19^h;
  July 12 8^h to July 13 2^h;
  July 24 11^h to 20^h *(also Magnolia);*
  Aug 19 21^h to Aug 20 11^h;
  Sep 4 20^h to Sep 5 5^h;
  Sep 20 11^h to Sep 21 5^h;
  Oct 3 12^h to Oct 4 6^h;
  Oct 31 16^h to Nov 1 10^h;
  Nov 18 10^h to 19^h *(also Magnolia).*
*Apple, **Apricot,** Copper beech, Damson, Maple, Olive, **Peach, Sweet chestnut,** Walnut:*
  April 16 17^h to April 17 11^h;
  June 3 12^h to June 4 6^h;
  June 22 22^h to June 23 16^h;
  July 12 8^h to July 13 2^h;
  Sep 6 1^h to 19^h;
  Sep 20 11^h to Sep 21 5^h;
  Oct 3 12^h to Oct 4 6^h;
  Oct 18 15^h to Oct 19 9^h;
  Oct 31 16^h to Nov 1 10^h.
Poplar, Sallow:
  Jan 13 17^h to Jan 14 3^h;
  Aug 19 21^h to Aug 20 11^h;
  (Nov 18 23^h to Nov 19 5^h).

*Ash, **Cedar, Fir,** Hazel, **Mirabelle plum,** Rowan, **Spruce:***
  May 17 4^h to 13^h;
  June 3 13^h to 22^h;
  June 22 22^h to June 23 16^h;
  July 15 3^h to 12^h;
  Sep 6 19^h to Sep 7 4^h;
  Sep 16 20^h to Sep 17 6^h;
  Sep 29 16^h to Sep 30 1^h;
  Nov 12 10^h to 19^h.
*Beech, **Cedar, Fir,** Hornbeam, Juniper, Palm, Pine, Plum, Quince, **Spruce,** Thuja:*
  March 21 15^h to March 22 6^h;
  May 12 13^h to 19^h;
  May 19 19^h to May 20 5^h;
  June 3 13^h to 22^h;
  Aug 23 6^h to 16^h;
  Sep 4 20^h to Sep 5 5^h;
  Sep 25 10^h to Sep 26 1^h;
  Sep 29 16^h to Sep 30 1^h.
*Birch, **Larch,** Lime tree, **Mirabelle plum,** Pear, Robinia, Willow:*
  Jan 13 17^h to Jan 14 3^h;
  May 6 4^h to 14^h;
  May 19 19^h to May 20 5^h;
  June 3 12^h to June 4 6^h;
  June 21 7^h to 17^h *(also Magnolia);*
  Aug 11 16^h to Aug 12 2^h;
  Aug 23 6^h to 16^h;
  Sep 6 1^h to 19^h;
  Sep 29 9^h to 19^h *(also Magnolia);*
  (Nov 18 23^h to Nov 19 5^h).
*Cherry, Chestnut, Horse chestnut (Buckeye), Oak, **Sweet chestnut,** Yew:*
  Feb 24 14^h to Feb 25 5^h;
  March 21 15^h to March 22 6^h;
  April 16 17^h to April 17 11^h;
  Aug 21 19^h to Aug 22 10^h;
  Sep 6 0^h to 15^h;
  Sep 25 10^h to Sep 26 1^h;
  Oct 18 15^h to Oct 19 9^h;
  Nov 29 2^h to 17^h.

The care of bees

A colony of bees lives in its hive closed off from the outside world. For extra protection against harmful influences, the inside of the hive is sealed with propolis. The link with the wider surroundings is made by the bees that fly in and out of the hive.

To make good use of cosmic rhythms, the beekeeper needs to create the right conditions in much the same way as the gardener or farmer does with the plants. The gardener works the soil and in so doing allows cosmic forces to penetrate it via the air. These forces can then be taken up and used by the plants until the soil is next moved.

When the beekeeper opens up the hive, the sealing layer of propolis is broken. This creates a disturbance, as a result of which cosmic forces can enter and influence the life of the hive until the next intervention by the beekeeper. By this means the beekeeper can directly mediate cosmic forces to the bees.

It is not insignificant which forces of the universe are brought into play when the hive is opened. The beekeeper can consciously intervene by choosing days for working with the hive that will help the colony to develop and build up its food reserves. The bees will then reward the beekeeper by providing a portion of their harvest in the form of honey.

Earth-Root times can be selected for opening the hive if the bees need to do more building. *Light-Flower* times encourage brood activity and colony development. *Warmth-Fruit* times stimulate the collection of nectar. *Water-Leaf* times are unsuitable for working in the hive or for the removal and processing of honey.

Since the late 1970s the varroa mite has affected virtually every bee colony in Europe. Following a number of comparative trials we recommend burning and making an ash of the varroa mite in the usual way. After dynamising it for one hour, the ash should be put in a salt cellar and sprinkled lightly between the combs. The ash should be made and sprinkled when the Sun and Moon are in Taurus (May/June).

Over the years I have come to sprinkle small amounts of ash on the brood to strengthen its effect whenever I carry out an inspection.

Spraying the varroa ash using a salt cellar

Biodynamic preparation plants

The biodynamic preparation plants are picked, dried, and inserted into animal sheaths (skull, bladder, etc.). *Maria Thun's log tree tree preparations* are made by inserting the plants into logs of certain trees instead of animal sheaths. The time of cutting the logs and inserting the dried plants is more critical than for traditional preparations, and therefore these times are given in the calendar. Both kinds are buried over winter to make the biodynamic compost preparations.

Pick *dandelions* in the morning at Flower times as soon as they are open and while the centre of the flowers are still tightly packed.

Pick *yarrow* at Fruit times when the Sun is in Leo (around the middle of August).

Pick *camomile* at Flower times just before midsummer. If they are harvested too late, seeds will begin to form and there are often grubs in the hollow heads.

Collect *stinging nettles* when the first flowers are opening, usually around midsummer. Harvest the whole plants without roots at Flower times.

Pick *valerian* at Flower times around midsummer.

All the flowers (except valerian) should be laid out on paper and dried in the shade.

Collect *oak bark* at Root times. The pithy material below the bark should not be used.

Fungal problems

The function of fungus in nature is to break down dying organic materials. It appears amongst our crops when unripe manure compost or uncomposted animal by-products such as horn and bone meal are used but also when seeds are harvested during unfavourable constellations: according to Steiner, 'When Moon forces are working too strongly on the Earth ...'

Tea can be made from horsetail *(Equisetum arvense)* and sprayed on to the soil where affected plants are growing. This draws the fungal level back down into the ground where it belongs.

The plants can be strengthened by spraying stinging nettle tea on the leaves. This will promote good assimilation, stimulate the flow of sap and help fungal diseases to disappear.

Moon diagrams

The diagrams overleaf show for each month the daily position (evenings GMT) of the Moon against the stars and other planets. For viewing in the southern hemisphere, turn the diagrams upside down.

61

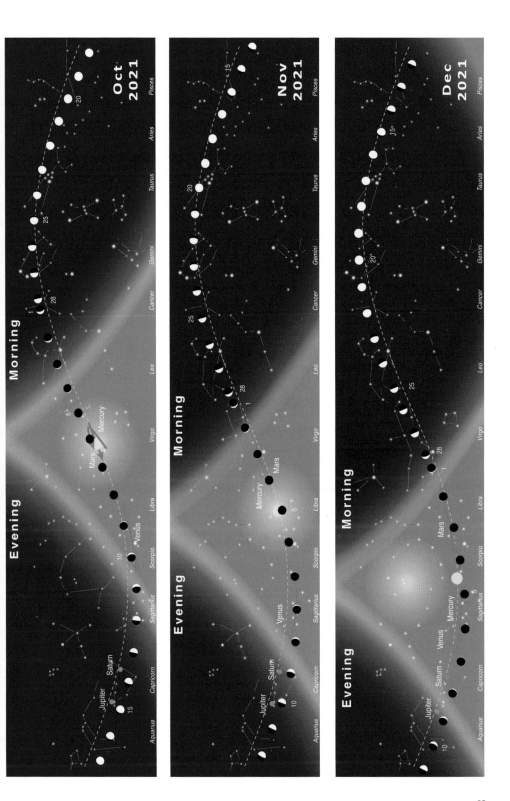

Further Reading

Berrevoets, Erik, *Wisdom of Bees: Principles of Biodynamic Beekeeping,* SteinerBooks, USA

Colquhoun, Margaret and Axel Ewald, *New Eyes for Plants,* Hawthorn

Karlsson, Britt and Per, *Biodynamic, Organic and Natural Winemaking,* Floris

Keyserlink, Adalbert Count von, *The Birth of a New Agriculture,* Temple Lodge

—, *Developing Biodynamic Agriculture,* Temple Lodge

Klett, Manfred, *Principles of Biodynamic Spray and Compost Preparations,* Floris

Klocek, Dennis, *Sacred Agriculture: The Alchemy of Biodynamics,* Lindisfarne

Koepf, H.H., *The Biodynamic Farm: Agriculture in the Service of Humanity,* SteinerBooks, USA

—, *Koepf's Practical Biodynamics: Soil, Compost, Sprays and Food Quality,* Floris

König, Karl, *Social Farming: Healing Humanity and the Earth,* Floris

Kranich, Ernst Michael, *Planetary Influences upon Plants,* Biodynamic Association, USA

Lepetit, Antoine, *What's so Special About Biodynamic Wine?* Floris

Masson, Pierre, *A Biodynamic Manual,* Floris

Morrow, Joel, *Vegetable Gardening for Organic and Biodynamic Growers,* Lindisfarne

Osthaus, K.-E., *The Biodynamic Farm,* Floris

Pfeiffer, Ehrenfried, *The Earth's Face,* Lanthorn

—, *Pfeiffer's Introduction to Biodynamics,* Floris

—, *Weeds and What They Tell Us,* Floris

—, & Michael Maltas, *The Biodynamic Orchard Book,* Floris

Philbrick, John and Helen, *Gardening for Health and Nutrition,* Anthroposophic, USA

Philbrick, Helen & Gregg, Richard B., *Companion Plants and How to Use Them,* Floris

Sattler, Friedrich & Eckard von Wistinghausen, *Growing Biodynamic Crops,* Floris

Selg, Peter, *The Agricultural Course: Rudolf Steiner and the Beginnings of Biodynamics,* Temple Lodge

Steiner, Rudolf, *Agriculture (A Course of Eight Lectures),* Biodynamic Association, USA (also published in another translation by Rudolf Steineer Press, UK)

—, *Agriculture: An Introductory Reader,* Steiner Press, UK

—, *What is Biodynamics? A Way to Heal and Revitalize the Earth,* SteinerBooks, USA

Storl, Wolf, *Culture and Horticulture,* North Atlantic Books, USA

Thun, Maria, *Gardening for Life,* Hawthorn

—, *The Biodynamic Year,* Temple Lodge

Thun, Matthias, *Biodynamic Beekeeping,* Floris

—, *When Wine Tastes Best: A Biodynamic Calendar for Wine Drinkers,* (annual) Floris

Weiler, Michael, *The Secret of Bees: An Insider's Guide to the Life of the Honeybee,* Floris

Wright, Hilary, *Biodynamic Gardening for Health and Taste,* Floris

Biodynamic Associations

Demeter International
www.demeter.net

Australia:
Australian Demeter Bio-Dynamic
demeterbiodynamic.com.au/
Biodynamic Agriculture Australia
www.biodynamics.net.au

Canada (Ontario): Society for Bio-Dynamic Farming & Gardening in Ontario
biodynamics.on.ca   (see also USA)

India: Bio-Dynamic Association of India (BDAI)
www.biodynamics.in

Ireland: Biodynamic Agriculture Association of Ireland
www.biodynamicagriculture.ie

New Zealand:
NZ Biodynamic Association
www.biodynamic.org.nz

South Africa: Biodynamic Agricultural Association of Southern Africa
www.bdaasa.org.za

UK: Biodynamic Association
www.biodynamic.org.uk

USA: Biodynamic Association of North America
www.biodynamics.com